Brian Nevill is a baby boom[...] in occupied Germany. Raise[...] suburbs of Surrey and Kent, he had a secondary modern education before beginning a career in varying jobs as a motor mechanic, estimating clerk, RAC itinerary planner, market gardener and warehouseman. At the age of nineteen, having played drums in semi-professional groups, he tried his hand at turning professional. When this gained him much experience but little remunerative reward, Brian returned to 'day' work. This period included publishing an underground newspaper and eventually moving to west London and working for a London underground paper. Selling records at his own indoor market stall on Portobello Road was followed by working in many of London's specialist record shops over the next few years. When the lure of playing music returned it led to Brian's longest period as a professional musician, travelling extensively and living in Europe and the United States. Another lull in his music career caused him to take on freelance music consultancy work, a role that brought writing back into Brian's life. Since 'retiring' from this, he has turned to his other first love, that of writing proper. *Boom Baby* is his first novel. He is married, has no children, has a large record collection, and lives in London.

Boom Baby

Boom Baby

*The escape from sixties
suburban culture*

BRIAN NEVILL

Published by
McZine

First published in Great Britain 2013
Text copyright © Brian Nevill
Cover design © Mark Jackson
Book design © Janette Revill

All photographs copyright Brian Nevill unless
otherwise stated. Every effort has been made to trace the
copyright holders of the photographs in this book.

The right of Brian Nevill to be identified as the author
of this work has been asserted by them in accordance with
the Copyright, Designs and Patents Act 1988.

McZine Publishing Limited
6 Lancaster Lodge
Lancaster Road
London W11 1QH

www.mczine.com

A CIP catalogue record for this book is
available from the British Library

Paperback ISBN: 9780957419834
e-Book ISBN: 9780957419841

Printed in Great Britain by
Clays Ltd, St Ives plc

All papers used by McZine Publishing are natural, recyclable
products made from wood grown in well-managed forests.
The manufacturing processes conform to the environmental
regulations of the country of origin.

For Lindy Loo, who knew me in a previous life,
and without whose encouragement . . .

Contents

Acknowledgements

My thanks to Chris Lansdowne, Chris Reeves and Linda Jenks for boundless support and a lot of help with my memory. To Kathleen Theresa Healy, Christine McDermott and John Blunt for allowing me to use their names and images and for their support. To Jennie Condell my editor, for believing and for being so creative with the pulling of teeth. To Lindy McDonnell, my wife, for her natural talent with editing and her patience. To Charlie Mounter for being the first reader of a rough manuscript and for her help. And last, but by no means least, my publisher McZine Publishing Limited.

And Then There Was Peace

For every rock star who trod a stage in one of England's music venues in the sixties, whose autobiography we now clamour for, there were thousands of punters who went home and copied the hairstyle, bought the album, looked in vain for the shirt, walked the walk and talked the talk. And went to work on Monday. Then listened to the album in the evening after standing for hours in front of a mirror teasing the hair into shape. Rode the bus into town hoping the summer heat would not spoil the crease in the trousers or the skirt. Boys and girls alike. Ready for the weekend, ready for the life.

Were the people born in time to consume in the fifties, sixties and seventies any different from those before or since? Yes, in that the teenager as we know it did not exist before the Second World War. The baby boomers exploded onto a stage that started at the end of austerity and crash-landed with the great consumer society. We came of age when there were more jobs than you could shake a stick at. And most of those millions of boomers only thought about getting a job for one purpose. Not a career, not a future. Only a way of acquiring the money to consume the vast new world of clothes, music, film, magazines, travel.

All this happened at the same time that the music, the clothes, the *styles* were the best we'd had before or have had since. Was it a coincidence? Was it just about timing or did we create it? The style has gone, as have the jobs. So that's that bookended then.

A friend of mine, someone who appears briefly in these pages, recently expressed his view on the decade that had seen both of us come of age. He said the sixties were like flowers growing out of a bombsite. If I may add to my friend's simile, the bombsite has now been flattened, and a block of concrete and glass stands on the space. The colours are now mostly beige. Style is a pop-up shop.

I don't care if the sixties dream is over. It was great while we dreamed, and although our aim was to share it, there were few takers. We left our legacy. Not that this little book is about any legacies at all.

It's about me, my pals and our girlfriends. Baby boomers. The faceless faces.

A Close Shave

'Anything for the prisoner?'

The officer seemed uninterested, preoccupied.

'Place the items on the counter, one at a time.'

I had a few items for the prisoner, all in a bag: a lot of sweets, some shaving soap and the doctored cigarette packet. Everything I handed over was entered into a book by the officer behind the glass. The cigarettes came last, and as I nonchalantly tossed the packet into the space between us the shrink-wrap popped open. Only a little, but . . . this is something that *does not happen* with factory-sealed cigarette packets.

The officer really hadn't seemed to notice, and I took a seat in the waiting room with the other visitors. It all seems to be all right, I told myself. I agonised over whether to get up and leave. I didn't know if it was an option. Instead I sat there and waited. And waited. The first sign of anything unusual was that I was the last person in the room by the time Porky's name was called.

At the beginning of 1972, at the age of twenty-four, following a couple of brushes with the law, I had moved into my mother's bungalow in leafy Selsdon, near Croydon. There was a new love in my life, Linda, who was also in the process of moving back into her parents' home. As soon as we found a flat we were going to be together.

Back hanging with some of the old crew, in the old familiar haunts (instead of continuing to lay low, which was the more sensible thing to do), I learned that one of my old mates, Porky,

3

had recently got himself into some serious trouble. He'd had a run-in with a gang outside a once-jolly, now running-to-seed Croydon pub called the Gun Tavern, protecting himself with a knife he carried because of the inevitability of such an attack (he had long been the target of a particularly nasty outfit since his days as the 'Prez' of a local Hells Angels chapter), and his adversary had come off rather badly. Consequently, Porky got done for attempted murder. Banged up in Brixton at Her Majesty's pleasure, he was on an extremely long remand, which would end in a long sentence.

I had not even seen Porky for nearly a year. Then I found myself having an afternoon beer with Joe Paris, another of my old cronies from the same clique. Joe, with a sunny disposition that belied his rough and ready image, had always sported the traditional Rocker look of leather jacket and tapered jeans throughout the changes in styles we'd seen over the years. A year ahead of me at my school, he had been a member of a gang called the Spoons, feared by pupils and teachers alike, had left home one morning a year before the legal school leaving age, and joined the Royal Navy. He was caught drug running in the Far East and was thrown out of the navy. Joe was never involved in dealing in civvy street, but he had a favour to ask me.

He and one or two others had been taking hashish into Brixton for Porky. It was Joe's turn to visit, but he couldn't go. With a feeling of tightness in the throat I said okay; there seemed no other answer. I had spent many, many days and nights in the company of this bunch of guys in all kinds of bent-out-of-shape states, and we always stood by each other. Long, stoned nights of listening to Dylan, laughing and philosophising with these ex-bikers had left me with perhaps a slightly warped notion of loyalty.

Later I picked up a packet of twenty cigarettes from Joe.

This is how it was done. A packet with a flip top had its plastic seal peeled off. Ten of the cigarettes were cut in half and before the filtered ends were placed back in the packet, a piece of hash the exact size and shape of ten half-cigarettes was placed in the gap. The packet was then re-sealed. That was the expert part, and they had done it three times already.

When the waiting room was completely empty, Porky's name was called.

I walked through with the guard and sat opposite the glass in front of my old friend, whose hair had not been butchered, and who looked well fed, a point that would have showed on Porky – he was a big feller from Geordie stock. We talked about all manner of things – his case coming up, and what had really happened to make him end up behind bars, as I had not been there and only heard stories – and I told him discreetly I had delivered a present for him. Then, as we were running out of things to chat about, I noticed we'd had well over the allotted half hour. Eventually, time was called on our visit, and Porky was led away as I turned to leave the room.

Just outside the door was the corridor back to the waiting room, where I immediately found myself between two men, one in front, one behind, who were restricting my progress along the corridor.

As we reached a door to our left one of them said, 'Just step in here, sir.'

Busted!

It was a long interview, the two officers taking it in turn to try and sweat out of me where I had scored the hash. There was enough of it to accuse me of dealing – except that, of course, I had been caught in the process of giving it away! I told them I had scored the dope from a stranger in a well-known Croydon pub, and it was my first attempt at delivering it to the prison; that I was thinking only of my friend, as I knew he occasionally smoked, so it would be a nice surprise. That he, in fact, had no idea I was going to do it. They swallowed my story.

I found myself in a cell, not for the first time, and my distraught mother had to come and bail me out, also not for the first time. I had ruined everything. There I was living at Mum's, looking for a flat with Linda, and next thing being told by our brief that I should not build up too much hope of not going down. It was a serious offence and I had some 'previous' with drugs.

After I had been nearly a month at my mother's, Linda and I found a flat in Streatham, and a man I met in a local pub arranged a boring job for me, out of the kindness of his heart, with a ladies' shoe manufacturer up in Whitechapel. Feeling slightly more confident about the court outcome with my new employment status, my day in Lambeth County Court was soon upon us. Not one of my friends attended; I wasn't even in a position to communicate with Porky. I didn't see Joe, avoidance seeming to be the best action all round. Funny what happens to loyalty and support sometimes.

It turned out that in 1972 there was no such thing as the offence of smuggling controlled drugs into Her Majesty's prisons. There was a law regarding smuggling of tobacco, food and 'contraband' generally. So the two offences they could do me for were smuggling tobacco and food and/or other items not listed, which carried a maximum sentence of a heavy fine; and, of course, possession of illegal drugs, which carried a maximum sentence of a stretch inside.

On the day, the usual magistrate, who I had been warned had a tough rep, was replaced by a trio of two men and one woman, which happens sporadically. There I was, neatly turned out, having removed an earring the size of a curtain ring, with my mother and girlfriend posed behind me in the public section for good effect. I received the maximum fine for the smuggling, and six months suspended over two years for the possession. I wasn't going to prison. My relief was overwhelming. I've never worn an earring since.

6

I chucked in that lousy job at the shoe factory straight away, just didn't show up on Monday. And something about the exuberance of unexpected freedom, and an overwhelming desire to flee the straitjacketed boredom of Streatham, made Linda and I propose to each other. We got married shortly after my court case, in a civil ceremony at Brixton, and celebrated with only a handful of close friends at our reception afterwards. Linda had stuck with me throughout the stress of my near escape, we had proved we were soul mates, and my south London days were now about to end forever.

But first, let me take you back. Back to the beginning, and some stories to tell.

Forty Miles of Bad Road

In May 1958, my best friend Chris Lansdowne turned ten. Our mothers were friends, and we had always been invited to each other's birthday parties organised by our mums. For Chris's birthday that May my parents had bought a Dinky Toy for me to give Chris. I collected them – most boys we knew did – so it was the obvious gift.

To this day Chris has it fixed in his memory that the model was a Cadillac – there was a much lusted-after Cadillac Eldorado made by Dinky. I, however, feel the car may well have been a Nash Rambler. Our American friends will probably grasp the irony here more than the Brits. As for Chris and I, we still argue about this kind of detail.

At this time Chris and I were going through the slow process of moving from model cars to female charms. All completely innocent, of course, but nevertheless there were girls we called our girlfriends. One such was a pretty blonde called Pat, a classmate of ours, and a resident of our estate. And she was Chris's 'girlfriend'. The notion still strikes me as a little comical, we romantic heroes in short trousers.

Chris was thrilled with the Dinky, and suspects he gave more attention to the gift than to his 'girlfriend', Pat, for the duration of his party. He certainly didn't seem to see much of her after that, in fact, although I remember chasing her around at school for a while myself. The concentration on an object of lust was shifting back and forth for both of us. There was Pat, a focal point during our playground games of awkward sexual discovery, taking a back seat in our mutual joy over a Dinky Toy. If Chris expected things to be the same when we got back to school, he was about to learn that women don't like taking second place.

Chris and I had been close friends from the time we were toddlers, and it was a natural friendship, one we never gave too much thought to. We went to the same primary and secondary schools, failed the same eleven-plus, and continued our friendship for a decade after school was out. We even shared more than one girlfriend (but not at the same time).

Our mothers had met at the local branch of the Women's League of Health and Beauty, which enjoyed a brief upsurge after the war. Gisela Nevill and Audrey Lansdowne were two young and strong women who were less than content with the drab reality of family life and who yearned for the opportunities of which they felt they had been robbed. A better life than that being offered to them on the post-war suburban plan.

Chris and I were going through the same thing. We shared the pressure put on us by parents wanting to achieve for *themselves*. Chris was made to go to church, and the church youth club. His mother influenced mine, which is why I attended Sunday school – for a while. They wanted us to be different from the other kids. We had to live out their dream.

The Nevills and Lansdownes, like so many others, had needed to pick up from where they'd left off in the damp and bright nineteen thirties world of the home counties. They shared with millions of parents the post-war need to work and raise a family in a functional suburban environment with new housing and new schools.

We were baby boomers.

* * *

9

My father, who was known by his second name, Roy (the same as mine), was born and raised in the Norwood area of south London, a booming suburb of neat, tree-lined avenues built in the thirties for young families to settle in, almost all of them renting from small local real estate firms. The house was a stone's throw from Selhurst Park, home ground of Crystal Palace Football Club, and nearby was Grange Woods, where I was told Dick Turpin had 'holed up' while on the run.

Dad was called up in 1942 at the age of eighteen, while his only brother, Claude, was too young, at fifteen, to go in. One day their little black cat, Dinky, died of fear in my uncle's arms during a bombing raid. That fixed it for my uncle; he lied about his age and got sent to Aden. Dad spent some time at Sandringham; he told me he winked at Princess Elizabeth when she came on an inspection of the troops with her sister. Very cheeky devil, my old man. Looking at these events from the vantage point of the present, I see myself in the passionate impulse of my uncle and the easy-going nonchalance of my dad. He would have a hard time 'fitting in', with his lanky frame, just short of six feet, shock of curly red hair and with a short fuse to match. He got posted to Holland, where he spent the rest of the war. He also spent a lot of time entertaining the troops, mostly G.I.s, with his swing piano playing.

After peace was declared Dad was stationed in Dortmund, Germany, with the British Army of the Rhine. This was where my mother was from. My maternal grandfather, Wilhelm Heinrich Gnass, who came from East Prussia, died before I was born. He was a musician and painter, wearer of fine clothes with broad-brimmed hats, owner of a substantially large and straight nose and fox-coloured hair, and father to four girls. I apparently strongly resemble my German grandfather. Once, in the early eighties, I visited Dortmund and stayed with my grandmother, as I was playing a gig nearby. At the time I was wearing my hair straight back from the forehead, and my grandmother nearly fainted when I walked in and doffed my hat. She thought it was her husband from long ago.

Gisela, my mother, was the eldest of the four girls, and seemingly, the one blessed with not only silver screen looks but a high level of education and a fierce ambition that contrasted with her five-foot-two frame. She was keen to escape the hell of a broken Germany, and, I've always felt, darker skeletons in the Gnass cupboard, bones that she would never share with me or anyone else. At twenty-three she got a job working for the British army at the barracks in Dortmund, as her English was faultless. Dad was a driver and bombardier, and his job was to ferry officers around in a Jeep or driving the truck at the front of a convoy – the one where the officer sticks his head up through a hole in the cab and makes signals to the trucks following. So he would see Mum in the officers' quarters, and that's how it got started, and how I got started. Dad was already engaged to a girl back in Thornton Heath. He wrote to his father, my English grandfather, asking him to 'pop' round and ask for his ring back. Outrageous, and so thought his fiancée's father! Grandad was given orders to piss off quickly. No return ring.

So my conception definitely came about through some lack of caution, and, although my parents went through a marriage ceremony in Düsseldorf, when Mum was getting a divorce years later, she discovered the marriage wasn't worth the paper it was printed on. There seems to have been an army blunder of some kind. It meant that the certificate was a sort of lie. There'll be a few of those in this story of mine.

I am a bastard – Mum told me this when she was getting that divorce – born in a British military hospital in Wuppertal, 4 January 1948, a Sunday. I was, apparently, the first Anglo-German baby to survive birth in that hospital. My birth certificate is a military one, dated Friday 13 February. Friday the thirteenth.

Life in the once great industrial Ruhr Valley under Allied rule was a struggle between the occupying powers tugging this way and that with differing policies, and a sullen local populace disgruntled with hunger and nobody making a move towards any kind of settlement and prosperous future for Germany. The soldiers stationed there got on with their orders and got on with the locals as best they could, including, somewhat disobediently, fraternising.

When my father was demobbed he was returned home; he had no choice in the matter. He immediately found work with Waterlow & Sons, the people who printed the *Radio Times* as well as banknotes. My mother and I came to Blighty later, in a storm in the English Channel that kept Mum awake while I slept the entire journey. We were reunited at my English grandparents' three-bedroomed rented house in Selhurst, south London. We lived there for a year, six adults and me. It was no picnic by all accounts. Mum, saddled with a baby and a strange family, which included a jealous sister, my aunty Doreen, became touchy and argumentative. Thinking about it, she never changed after that!

After a frustrasting year cramped in the space of that family home, Dad was advised to 'lower his standards' in order to get moved up the council waiting list. In other words, Croydon County Council regarded our situation as too high a standard to be eligible for council accommodation any time soon. So the three of us moved out of Grandma's house and into one room in West Wickham in leafy suburban Kent. People fortunate enough to own property were renting out rooms to the displaced new families roaming the land. It was probably not a moment too soon for Dad's family. Although I was around two years old, my first memories stem from this time. And, believe it or not, my young mind was aware I was living with a troubled and unhappy couple. From there we waited until they had almost finished building a new housing estate called New Addington.

Garden Village

After we had spent about a year in that one room I was wheeled in a pushchair by my young parents the few miles from those pruned streets to the muddy hopeful southern extreme of New Addington, and a maisonette on King Henry's Drive that would be my home until I was twenty.

New Addington dates back to the 1930s. Before the estate was built the land on which it now stands was farmland belonging to Castle Hill, Addington Lodge and Fisher's farms, and the nearest village was Addington. New Addington was intended to be a 'Garden Village', with a few thousand houses, shops, churches, a cinema and a village green. There were several reasons behind this plan, one of them being the pressing need for Croydon to clear many of the older slum areas that had been created during the Depression.

After the war had suspended construction of the original idea, and with 55,000 people now on the waiting list, building started again. The first step was to erect a few hundred prefabs for homeless families, and these were in place by 1948. The prefabs, plus large areas of overgrown rough land and surrounding woods, were all still there throughout my growing up. In the case of the prefabs, they are mostly still there. It seems that in the immediate post-war years temporary housing was built to last! No cinema was ever built; when I finally got to see, in my teens, the early Elvis Presley films from the fifties, they were shown at the community centre. There was one long snake of a shopping

14

street called Central Parade, while there were smaller rows of shops dotted throughout the estate. There seemed to be dozens of schools: Overbury, Fairchildes, Rowdown, Good Shepherd (a Catholic school – Catholics were our minority group in the fifties). Overbury and Fairchildes, the latter which Chris and I attended, were friendly rivals. We had no grammars; they were all on the way in to Croydon, the nearest town proper, and a half-hour bus ride away. There were a few churches, including one, St Edwards, built when I was a pre-teen, which held the dreaded Sunday school ('We missed you last Sunday, Brian'). A few youth clubs sprang up: some, like the Goldcrest, built specially. There was one factory estate too, called Vulcan Way.

Surrounding most of our homes was a lot of waste ground, weedy paths leading to other weedy paths. With the first-floor maisonette that became our address we had an enormous garden, unmade when we moved in. Here Dad would fight a flinty enemy, caused by the dumping of broken stones during the estate's extensive building, with which he got precious little help from his son. At the bottom of the garden was yet another weedy way, along which our neighbours would pass. Beyond that were trees and a fence separating us from huge fields, which were in Kent. The county border was at the bottom of our garden.

New Addington always felt more like part of Kent than Surrey – that is, rough-hewn and raggedy rural, where Surrey is stockbroker and tidy. Between Addington and Croydon lay upper-middle-class home-owner manors like Sanderstead, Purley and Selsdon, which suggested Surrey entirely. Go to Addington on a bright day, and the same thing will strike you today as struck me when I was walking those post-war streets: *no shade*. There is no shade – anywhere. The rough open spaces have been tidied and landscaped, but not built upon. There was obviously no need; there was so much space. But that illustrates how much space was needed *back then*.

New Addington enjoyed the nickname 'Little Siberia', because for some reason it was seriously cold in the winter. I can remember sometimes walking along crying as hailstones that really stung rained down with a cold easterly wind. When snow lay thick on the roads, buses would stop at the bottom of the steeper hills, let the passengers off, and then climb the incline with the passengers walking beside the bus to the top.

And across these vast wastes I would walk as I grew up. I would walk to the streets where my first girlfriends lived. To the streets where my friends lived. Across the great spaces to my first group rehearsals. Sometimes I found myself just walking . . . nowhere.

There was, and still is, only one major road in to New Addington: Lodge Lane, bringing you in, through the suburbs, from Croydon to the north. A sign on Lodge Lane used to say 'Drive With Care: 30,000 Children.' Yeah, but no cinema and no swimming pool until the mid-sixties, just a funfair twice a year.

And I sprang up in this sprawling development of 30,000 children. My mother had made the decision for both herself and my father to limit our family to the one child. Not for any medical reason – she apparently just announced after my birth, 'Never again.' And her ambition to 'do well' remained all-consuming. This meant that, although her drive for fastidious child-rearing was focused on her only child, Mum started work the week I began school, embarking on a career in private secretarial work. This wasn't unusual; we lived in a world where women were taking to work out of necessity, unaware of the revolution in the workplace they were sparking.

I was farmed out to various families from the age of five. This meant being dropped off somewhere before school, and making my way back to the same address afterwards, having tea with someone else's family, then getting picked up by Mum and walked home. No cars.

This was all a generally hateful experience for me, and led to me distancing myself from other children. I was surly, unresponsive and more than a little sensitive. I rarely liked other children, and none of the first carers lasted more than a few weeks. I grew to be at my happiest when all alone. The weeds and dusty roads of New Addington were the backdrop to the plays going on in my head, as I invented stories with a consuming enthusiasm.

The Bug Hop

Grandma and Aunty Doreen lived alone in the Selhurst house as Grandad had died in 1957, and Dad's brother, my favourite uncle, got married as Grandad was dying. So the house had emptied itself suddenly of men and left Grandma and my aunty.

By 1958, I had started to spend some time in the school holidays with Grandma. My friends were a piano, reams of paper, an old gramophone that played 78s, scrapbooks, paste and scissors, cats, Dinky toys from Town's Toy Town, comics and above all, Grandma. I never wanted anything else. I even used to enjoy the walks every other day down to the High Street with Gran. She would spend quite a bit of time doing herself up, *always* wore a hat with a pin. All the way to the High Street we would have to stop and talk to people, as nearly everyone in the neighbourhood knew Mrs Nevill. They would always admire the outfits my mother had me dress in, little velvet-collared coats like Prince Charles.

Aunty Doreen also bought me clothes, which she enjoyed doing as she would never have children of her own. The clothes she bought me were more to my own taste, and this would exacerbate the conflict that existed between the 'sister' and the 'wife', sometimes leading to loud and violent rows between Mum and Aunty Doreen, much to the embarrassment and confusion of my young mind. Mum lived in the fear that if Doreen had her way, I'd be dressed like the little yobbo I seemed to aspire to be. I remember a screaming row they had about a tie my aunty had bought me, one I had picked out. When Mum saw it, she blew a fuse.

'Before you know it, he's going to look like Tommy Steele!'

The tie was brought back to our own house, packed in a drawer, and never spoken of again. For a few years I would occasionally sneak into my parents' bedroom, open one of their drawers and just look at that tie. There was a little jewel of red glass right in the centre of the shiny silver fabric, and it seemed to glint up and wink at me.

When Gran and I would get to the High Street we had to stop at a seemingly endless number of shops and stalls. All the groceries had to be bought from different places; there was no supermarket down that High Street then. I remember the saucy blokes on the stalls and the way they bantered with Gran, and the cool atmosphere at the David Greig delicatessen counter – probably called a dairy then. Everything would be handed over in thick greaseproof wrapping paper.

When we got back from the High Street I would settle down to pasting in a scrap book with paste Gran had made for me, play the piano for an hour or so, or just read my new comics. Then we'd have lunch together and she would fall asleep in front of the horse racing on television. Sometimes she would have washing to do. This, folks, was a house with no bathroom; the bath was in the kitchen, which involved much shifting around on bath nights. Grandma's washing was done in a zinc tub with a washboard, just like the ones they used in skiffle groups. And to heave the wet clothes out of the tub she would use a drumstick, a leftover from when Uncle Claude had learned drums and used the entire house as his drum kit, something they couldn't afford to buy him. To wring the clothes ready for the clothes line in the back garden, Grandma used an old-fashioned mangle that stood in the lean-to next to the kitchen. She must have had the strength of two men, that little woman.

Meanwhile, every Monday we went to the pictures, because she could get in for 1/3d on her pension. My aunty paid for us. We would meet her for lunch at a restaurant in North End, Croydon, called the Merrie Kettle, yes, spelled that way, where I always had pea soup. It was old fashioned even then, one of those places with white tablecloths and waitresses with white aprons. Then Gran and I would get a bus or train to whichever picturehouse was showing a 'U' picture on general release. Once there, Grandma would fall straight to sleep and I would nudge her for half the film before giving up.

Early in 1959 we saw the explosive Frankie Vaughan in *The Lady Is a Square*, which also starred Anthony Newley, of whom I became a fervent fan. I was even taken to see Frankie live at Bournemouth Winter Gardens, where he was much more sedate than he normally appeared on television. Aunty had been a huge fan since Frankie had taken over from Liberace in her heart. Tommy Cooper was on that bill too. The summer of 1959 we saw *The Five Pennies* with Danny Kaye and Louis Armstrong. That must have been the first film I got emotional about. Although the first film I remember thinking about for any length of time was *3:10 to Yuma* with Glenn Ford. That is when I realised that a Western could be more than just shoot-'em-up cowboys and Indians. Ford's intense demeanour, operating at a slower pace than anyone else in the film, made me want to be a man just like him; very bad but with a good heart and a sense of honour. Growing up! There was an endless stream of Doris Day vehicles and then in the summer of 1962 we saw *Some People* with David Hemmings, the impressive Ray Brooks and the squeaky-clean Kenneth More. This was my first 'teenage' movie, and I felt it was talking directly to me. I even created and drew my own comic book called *Something to Do*, which ripped off the plot of *Some People*. Oh yes, the reams of paper – that's what I used to do with them. My aunty used to bring the paper home from work, which was early computer stuff – I think they called it a comptometer. I made my own comics. Folded the paper so it worked like a comic book, and started from the first page, the first frame. Just made up the stories as I went along, no planning. I created a lot of Westerns, sometimes created funny animals, and in the case of this latest effort, a story about teenagers in a rock group. But that film, it even had good music.

I truly loved my grandma. Regrettably she took the full brunt of my teen psychosis in the years to come, as I later turned into a kid with a very spoilt and precocious streak. I used to bait her with any argument I could think of, even in the midst of her spoiling me so. She was very patient with me, even when I was upsetting her. I think she probably knew I was venting some pent-up emotions caused by the restrictions put on me by my own mother. I like to think I had largely got over most of that before I stopped staying at Grandma's house. I certainly would call on her unexpectedly from time to time for the rest of her life. She had these sayings that seemed to have come from another world altogether, such as, 'In the oven behind the rice'; 'Laugh to see a puddin' crawl'; and 'How's yer belly off fer spots?' Grandma died when I was twenty-three. I was inconsolable.

* * *

There was a red-hot summer in 1958. That year a group of modern jazz fanatics decided to adopt a tag to differentiate themselves from the growing army of 'trad' fans. They called themselves Modernists. Trad had grown from the New Orleans revival that had proliferated after the war in Britain, and 'modern' at the time meant bebop jazz *à la* Charlie Parker and cool Californian sounds *à la* Gerry Mulligan. Trad followers tended to swallow copious quantities of cider and were habitués of cellar clubs where they could dress scruffily. Many of the original trad fans had adopted a duffle coat-and-sandals look and acquired the handle of 'Beats'. This handle derived from their reading material, the early works of Kerouac and Ginsberg. Modernists leaned towards the sharp and the cool. They began wearing a sharpened-up version of the Italian 'bum-freezer' suit that had replaced the Edwardian look of the Teddy boys, as the Modernists emulated the black American musicians they admired. This American influence led them to wear imported 'Ivy League' clothing, like button-down shirt collars with slim ties. Rather than reading, the Modernists would spend much of their time studying French new wave cinema. As for us kids living in the heat of the suburban 1958 summer, we were only really aware of the Ted-type variety of teenager, as were the tabloid press of the time.

During that August my parents took me to Germany for our first visit since we had all left ten years before. When I got back to school one kid asked me how long the journey took. I thought about it, and as we had taken the overnight ferry from Harwich to the Hook of Holland, I told him two days. He said, 'You're a liar, it would take much longer than that.'

We were baby boomers; we hadn't been abroad yet.

It Doesn't Matter Anymore

After it had not worked out with another family looking after me, an arrangement was made with our next-door neighbours, the Dipples – an obvious choice, as they were already good friends. In fact my parents were uncharacteristically neighbourly with the Dipples, who had been on the estate as long as we had. They were wonderful people, and their oldest son Colin and I became good friends. He was a school year younger, but Colin and I shared a certain aloneness, especially in the years before his little brother was born. We played together; I brought my little soldiers, cowboys and Dinkies over to his house and we joined forces. Then we grew into pop fans, both being smitten by Cliff Richard on television. Our tastes in rock 'n' roll differed somewhat as time went by, he leaning towards the smoother Bobby Vees and me towards the hard-edged Eddie Cochrans, but we overcame these differences enough to create our own pop magazine, read by his dad alone, I think. At school we did not see each other because of the year difference, but at Colin's house we spent some magic hours between getting home from school and his mum, Peggy, getting in and making our tea. We discovered the opposite sex at about the same time, and shared our fantasies. The only one I kept a secret was that I lusted after Peggy more than a little. Raging hormones.

Meanwhile, we were all edging towards saying goodbye to Fairchildes Junior School. This meant the dreaded eleven-plus was looming large. It was the first important test we kids had to face in those days, and something our parents took more seriously than we did. At least mine did. They let me know, in no uncertain terms, that they expected me to pass and go on to glory at a grammar school. Pile on the pressure, folks!

* * *

My last term at junior school ended in summer 1959. Chris Lansdowne and I were among a group from our year whose parents had paid up to send us on a school trip abroad. These foreign trips were a new innovation, bringing culture to the comprehensive ranks, even before holidays abroad had become the norm for working-class and middle-class Britain. A coachload of us went to Holland and Belgium on a trip organised in conjunction with the Youth Hostels Association. It was us, a group of mixed eleven year-olds, and a class of teenage girls from Fairchildes Secondary Modern Girls' School, a mass of frothy petticoats and cheap scent. Chris and I sat as far back in the coach behind our group and nearer to the older girls as we could.

The main thing the girls did was sing most of the time we were on the coach. A song they sang every day was in the hit parade at the time, but for some reason had until now escaped my attention. It began, 'There you go, baby, here am I . . .', and the chorus went, 'I guess it doesn't matter anymore'. At the time, as well as having not heard the tune, I had never heard of Buddy Holly. Later that year I learned that one of my future idols had been killed the previous February. The song the girls had sung had entered the UK charts late that month and was still there when we were touring round Holland. Thanks, girls. Buddy and the Crickets had played the Davis Theatre in Croydon in 1958, so I guess they made a big impression on Croydonians. I wish I had been old enough to go. The Crickets also appeared on Sunday Night at the London Palladium in March 1958, and although I sat up and watched pretty much every one of those, I have no memory of that one. It's hard to picture Buddy, Jerry and Joe going round on that revolving rostrum at the end of the show with Tommy Trinder.

As the trip had been organised through the Youth Hostels Association, we were made to perform certain tasks. The one we all dreaded was spud bashing. Chris and I scored spud peeling duty on the same day. There were hundreds of potatoes in a barrel of cold water, into which we had to plunge our lily white arms, and after peeling the spuds, drop them into another barrel of 'finished' products.

From time to time a woman in charge of the kitchen would appear to inspect the potatoes in the finished barrel. As, of course, our work was a little less than thorough, she would stare at the example she had pulled out of the barrel, and in her limited English, shout, 'Look! The eyes! They look to me!'

Just fourteen years after the end of the war, the breakfasts seemed luxurious compared to what most people in England were having. Different breads, cheese and cold meat slices, real coffee, a little different from our toasted Sunblest and marmalade with soggy Cornflakes! On this and future trips to Europe we were always amazed at the seeming speed of recovery after the degradation of the war over there, compared to Old Blighty lagging behind.

* * *

After this holiday along came the eleven-plus results, something I had blithely forgotten about during the holidays. Oh dear. Instead of spending the next few years at one of Croydon's grammar schools, followed by some prestigious college and an illustrious career, I was going to turn up at Fairchildes Secondary Modern School for Boys, and spend the next five years there. My parents were crushed by this fact, to an extent I could not fathom. Dad let me know that I was below par as far as intelligence was concerned, and had not come up to his expectations – it seemed I was not in line with his own achievements at school. He always seemed to be bitter about something. Mum just went into overdrive, trying to research the possibilities of finding me an alternative education with no money. She had heard of something called the thirteen-plus which I could go in for in two years' time, but nothing came of that. Bear in mind my mother was so ambitious for me that she took me to elocution lessons for an embarrassing few months, where I had to stand and 'enunciate' for a kindly middle-aged lady in her parlour in the rear of an overfurnished egg-and-polish-smelling semi-detached, to attempt to undo the effects of going to school on a post-war council estate.

'The rain in Spain falls mainly on the plain.'

Needless to say, the elocution lessons made no difference whatsoever to the way I spoke. Any child understands deep down that to blend in with the others is to lead an unworried and happy life, and running around sounding like a public schoolboy can only happen in a public school. Thanks for the humiliation, Mum.

One joyous thing that emerged from the eleven-plus failure was that on the first day at the big new school, we saw all our mates from the little old school. The fact was that all children coming through the B-stream in primary school would fail the eleven-plus, while all those who had spent their junior schooling in the A-stream would pass. There were a handful of exceptions to this, but, by and large, here was the proof that decisions had been made many years before the exam, on our behalf.

With this in mind, Colin, my little mate next door, said, 'Never mind, I'll be joining you next year.' Here was the irony. The following year came, and, lo, Colin passed the exam. No-one was more surprised than he, with the exception of his parents, who added elation to their surprise. My own parents kicked into disappointment all over again. At least Dad did, for whom this was a gross injustice. After all, Colin with more brains than his own son? His father was a milkman, for Chrissake! And Colin's dear father, the most lovable cockney to come out of the Arsenal with the baby boom rush, was over the moon. And he laid it on thick. I remember him trotting up their garden path shouting, 'My son's got brains!' It was for my father's benefit, and he had it coming.

As much as that long-ago exam could divide two friends, it was our generation who instinctively knew that it had nothing to do with brains. We understood that it was an institutional form of selection, not natural selection.

I continued to have my tea at the Dipples' until I was about thirteen, when I became trusted enough to be given a key to my own front door. Until then my great friendship with Colin continued, as did our shared enthusiasm for rock 'n' roll, especially Buddy Holly. It made no difference that we didn't see each other at school, as we were a year apart anyway. The radio was useless at that time, but there was a good show with Sam Costa on the BBC Light Programme just around teatime, which would be the only one we listened to together. After that it would have to be Radio Luxembourg, which I spent hours attempting to tune into on our radiogram between the hours of Mum arriving and Dad coming home, which would often signal the end of my radio activity. Even after my move into the responsible world of preparing my own tea, Colin and I did stuff together. We had a little rock group, just us and Colin's little brother, Oxo tins and rubber bands taking the place of real instruments. After my 'move' Colin announced he was learning to play drums at school and I felt the first twinge of a distance between us, as by the time I was fourteen I was forming a rock group at school myself, with me as the drummer, and this would mean a rivalry that could not be easily contained. Colin wasn't that normal a grammar school boy, although the difference in our ages, the fact of my new independence, and that we had our own set of friends, meant that we drifted apart in our early teens. One day the Dipples moved, lock, stock and barrel to Stamford Hill, Colin's dad's old manor. We went up in our new car one day to visit, but after that I never saw any of them again.

* * *

The beginning of secondary modern education was also the start of serious teenhood. Some of us had been training our hair into inventive sculptures while we were still in junior school, but now we had the added problem of *school uniform*. It was not absolute law at our sec mod, as it would have been at a grammar, but it brought up other divisions, like that between those who wore uniform, and those who did not. Those who did not being either too poor or too cool.

The biggest problem for me was trousers. Most boys' mothers had them in long trousers in time for the new big school. Again, it was not law, and there were many of us who attended the new school in shorts for most of the first and even second terms. My trouble was that I was much taller than most of my classmates. I was an object of derision outside school, when I happened to be passing some of the local teenagers that lived over in Grandma's more urban patch in south London. Some teachers had even started to mention it might be time for me to be moving into a lengthier trouser by now. Yeah, but when it's up to your mum, what are you supposed to do?

My main concern was that when I eventually got my first long trousers, they would be too wide. Glancing with a critical eye over the more sartorial lads in the fourth, it was apparent that the *de rigueur* ankle measurement was sixteen inches. *At the most.* In my mind I could see a pair of jet-black gabardines ending in turn-ups at a sixteen-inch bottom. Eventually I went shopping with Mum and came home with my new school trousers, in grey Terylene with turn-ups, and fucking *eighteen*-inch bottoms! No matter that I acquired compliments on my smartness from certain masters, it was only compared with the poor slobs who took no sartorial interest, and whose parents took even less.

Those grey offenders were the first and last, happily. The following year or so saw a trend for a narrower trouser, fourteen inches at the ankle, with the turn-up having disappeared. The Shadows ruled for the boys who fancied themselves as members of a guitar group, as well as anyone wanting to look contemporary, as the Shads were always dressed so sharp and so up-to-the-minute. The waistband was lower, with no pleats, with pockets that slanted across almost parallel with the waistband. At the outer corners of these pockets would be little slit openings. These pockets necessitated a stance with the elbows thrust forward when one's hands were in one's pockets, which they usually firmly were, the whole effect ending in a mincey swagger. The little slits were extended to the trouser bottoms in the case of some more adventurous boys who could get away with it. I remember that all my trousers seemed to be cut from a rough fabric that continually chafed the inner thigh. This was the era of the Italian bum-freezer suit and outside school (and sometimes even in) one could see guys with little cloth-covered buttons at the apex of the ankle slits. At the lower extremities, of course, were the most exaggerated winkle-pickers. We all wore as pointed a pair of shoes as we could; I remember when the chisel toe reached our suburban hamlet, around 1961, a long time after its invention in the urbane urban world.

Mention should be made of the way the Italian suit was viewed in the suburbs. In the urban areas of London it had been the original Modernists who had evolved into this style away from the Edwardian look, where the cascading Brylcreemed Tony Curtis slowly became the 'college boy'. But if you lived seven miles out, on the rural side of Croydon, the fellers who adopted the new look mostly were the same fellers who had worn the draped look a year earlier, the last of the Teds. Where I lived all young men who dressed fashionably and looked as if they were not unfamiliar with trouble were called Teddy boys long after the style had morphed into the Italian style. Our lads, however, would mix the styles in such a way as to, for instance, go out and about in a new off-the-peg dogtooth Italian 'shorty' suit with steel toe-capped hobnail boots! We called these chaps 'hardnuts'.

My own trouserwear progressed along with an increased itchiness. At the age of thirteen I had a pair of cavalry twill strides in cream with turn-ups, which had been my choice, a compromise with Mum. But they were still aggravatingly rough. Meanwhile, back at the very beginning of all this sec mod style confusion, the item that separated the boys from youths the most was the shirt.

There was a chap in my class who I had known since junior school, called Little Phil. Phil had had two older brothers before him in the secondary school, and hence a knock-on reputation that exacerbated his natural tendency towards laziness and general hatred of authority. He did not last out the second year – some activity, involving the riding of a motorcycle that he was not the owner of, while underage and unlicensed, and, oh yes, breaking the speed limit, earned him a place at a more 'specialist school'. Before all this he had appeared at school one day wearing a black shirt. The height of cool! One master went as far as to ask Phil if he wore a black shirt because he thought it needed less washing. *What!?* Our mothers do the washing, sir! How far away from comprehending the need to wear a black shirt can a square get? It was shortly after this that somehow I persuaded my parents to buy me a *red* shirt. Now, we are talking full-on one hundred per cent Elvis Presley red. Black and red were the two cool options, and I had lucked out with the latter. Poking our modern noses into this story from the vantage point of today, you have to remember that these were the grey and dull days in England before the advent of visiting French students; imported European clothes; before any of us had seen gay men and the colourful clothes they wore (and which were a direct influence on Carnaby Street). In 1960, a red shirt said things for you. It was the greatest piece of clothing I had ever owned in my life. Of course, I could not wear it to school. But I was wearing it one day when Phil paid a visit to our maisonette to see if I was available to escape my mother and have some fun. I was not, but we chatted at the door for a while, and he was very impressed, very envious and very inquisitive about my red shirt. Made it! By the way, if I'd been allowed to go out with Phil that night I would probably have joined him at the 'specialist school'.

The other main concern for boys of around thirteen is girls. My closest friend of the teenage years, Chris, was also my main introducer to the fairer sex. Now, by this I do not mean to suggest *sex*. I mean the fairer sex. We were still in the junior school playground when Chris instigated playing 'Kiss Chase'. This was a game with incredibly simple rules, a game whose name suggests all one needs to know about the procedure. I always allowed Chris to pick our fellow players; he had the best taste. Pat, who had appeared at Chris's birthday party, was a must-have for the team.

The biggest shock, and I do mean shock, for us boys upon starting secondary school was that it was sexually segregated. I for one was a gangling and shy loner who was just weighing up the difference between the precocious and pretty girls who giggled in my face, and the friendly ones who I found I could make laugh. Ah, the power of humour! Another disadvantage with being an only child is that all kids of one's own age are aliens until you can break the spell of communication. And just at this point they took the fairer sex away for four or five years, depending on how long you stayed for the sec mod experience.

Our first teenage parties would have been around the age of

thirteen, if Ernie K-Doe's 'Mother-in-Law' is anything to go by. By teenage party I mean, of course, where the parents are out for the evening. The main game played at these affairs was 'Postman's Knock'. Just about this time the twist became the dance craze. I bought Bobby Darin's 'Multiplication', a record of which both sides are twist tunes, but I did not go in for too much else on the twisting side as far as my record shopping went. What I did do, however, was learn to twist very well. This was my way of being sociable at parties, and it even spread over to the adult parties my mother was beginning to throw. When I say adult, I don't mean *adult*, I mean grown-up. The twist was my main way of overcoming a shyness exacerbated by being an only child, and also the fact that no-one had taught me to dance.

A couple of years earlier I had been asked to sing a Cliff Richard song for some relatives, and I had nearly died a thousand deaths with embarrassment. But I could twist my way around your little proverbial. I regret that my lack of older siblings or any cousins had robbed me of the necessity of learning to jive, that dance so many of my peers could do, which the twist supplanted while introducing the free-form style for the 'swinging sixties' yet to come. My inability to dance would hamper me more in my affairs with the fairer sex at the dance halls I would frequent through till the mid-sixties.

Aunty Doreen said to me more than once, 'You need to learn three things: dancing, tennis and swimming.' Oh dear, Aunty, I failed one hundred per cent.

The twist was still alive and twisting when we started to attend youth clubs in about 1961–62. Another popular dance at the youth clubs, something that seems not to have existed outside of them, was called the line bop. Purveyors of what is now known as the stroll would recognise the basic idea. Back then it was boys and girls alike, forming a long line with one's mates and remembering where you were.

Permit me to return briefly to that first year at secondary. There was another little freedom that presented itself: school dinners. You have to remember that all working-class people and working-class schools called lunch dinner, and dinner tea. School dinner cost our parents one shilling. So we would have a dinner register taken in the morning after the attendance register, and pay our humble shilling. Except that a little bunch of us would keep the shilling and not register. This meant we were free for a glorious hour at lunchtime (aka dinner time), with the princely sum of one shilling to spend.

My main accomplice during the one hour of freedom was a boy called Vic Leppard. Vic wore Buddy Holly-style specs and lived in a maisonette just like the one I lived in. Chris Lansdowne was quite often the only other member of our one-hour club. At the little parade of shops near the school there was a newsagent who would sell single cigarettes for tuppence each. For some reason they were called Tuppenny Masters. So our shilling would divide up into one Tuppenny Master, a bottle of a fizzy amber pop called Fling and a measure of the sliced sausage known in those days as luncheon meat.

Round at Vic's maisonette we would spend the lunch hour spinning his meagre collection of records. This meant the few fairly cool choices we could find among the haul in his cupboard. There was a greasy copy of Tommy Steele's 'Rock With The Caveman' on a 45, the obligatory Lonnie Donegan EPs, one with the great 'Stewball' on it, another with 'Dead or Alive', another favourite, and an EP that had lost its sleeve featuring selections from *Carmen Jones*, from which we liked 'Beat Out Dat Rhythm on a Drum'. Best of all was a 78 of 'Rock Around the Clock'. Now, this record was already so old it was considered an antique, but we found it still exciting and played it to death. The big favourite, however, was the other side, 'Thirteen Women'. Vic convinced me of its greatness. Trouble was, there was a chunk out of the edge of this side of the 78, which was a common problem with shellac, and we had to place the stylus down a little way into the track. For years after that I never knew the beginning of Bill Haley's 'Thirteen Women'.

Sometimes we would go round to mine. My parents' record selection was even worse. We had acquired our first radiogram in 1958, and so far I had bought a Duane Eddy 45, and the rest of the collection at this point consisted of sickly orchestral pop that Dad liked, some Dixieland jazz that both my parents liked and some classical, some of it mine. They did have a Perry Como 45, and as this was pretty uptempo, I played it for the lads once and tried to get away with telling them it was Elvis. It didn't work, and Vic said, 'If that *was* Elvis, you wouldn't be able to understand the words.' *Right.*

It was in 1960, with the advent of pocket money, that I started buying my own records. I bought the Drifters, Fats Domino, the Shadows and, at last, Elvis . . . I was on my way.

New Orleans on Oxford Street

In 1961 my parents took me to the Marquee Club on Oxford Street. Trad jazz, as it was known, was the only real crossover point in music between my parents. Mum liked classical but also had a penchant for schlock, like carols and schmaltzy pop. Kind of two extremes, but then she did bring the first Elvis LP into the house, even though it was *G.I. Blues*, featuring the new tame Elvis, so she could hear 'Wooden Heart'. Dad liked instrumental lounge music and leaned towards the smoother side of jazz, later on discovering Nashville and turning into a country fan for the rest of his life. This had probably already happened by 1961, as we had Jim Reeves, Marty Robbins, Hank Locklin and Floyd Cramer in the charts, as well as at home. But trad was my parents' meeting ground.

It was most likely Mum's idea to pursue a live show. I think she had heard about venues like the Six Bells pub, in Chelsea's World's End, from work colleagues. The records Mum and Dad had bought in this genre were mostly Chris Barber and Humphrey Lyttelton, both top gear as far as I was concerned, although Dad had ventured into the more commercial side of the trend too. It was decided to catch Chris Barber, and to this end Dad brought a copy of *Melody Maker* home – he had been a reader in his own youth, until his conscription in 1942, so for him it was the obvious choice. And it was the right one, being the main jazz paper at the time. The ads in the back led the three of us on the path to Oxford Street. It was also the beginning of my being an avid reader of

MM, having it saved for me at a local newsagent until I left home at the age of twenty.

The Marquee on Oxford Street was in the basement of number 165, under what was called the Academy Cinema, an early home for political and art house movies. The building also included a restaurant called the Pavillion, and the Marquee ballroom in the basement had held dances with big bands in the early fifties. By late 1957 the club was featuring jazz nights at the weekend and the first 'Jazz at the Marquee' night was held on 4 January 1958, my tenth birthday, although of course no-one concerned knew or cared about that – and I wasn't to visit for another three years. The Marquee started out featuring exclusively jazz and skiffle acts, one of which, the Chris Barber Jazz Band, virtually held a residency when they were in town. The décor of the place was designed by theatre set designer Angus McBean, and its red and white stripes were intended to represent a circus marquee, giving the ballroom its name. The theme was carried over to the second, and more famous, Marquee venue, on Wardour Street in Soho in 1964.

The success of the Marquee, and that of Chris Barber, was largely owed to Harold Pendleton, who arrived from Merseyside in 1948 (what a year!), becoming Barber's manager and the eventual owner of the Marquee. He also became the secretary of the burgeoning National Federation of Jazz Organisations of Great Britain (NJF), formed by musicians, critics and club owners to raise the standard of live jazz in London. In 1958 Pendleton brought Muddy Waters to the UK, where he played an electric guitar at the Roundhouse pub at the end of Old Compton Street, with Walter Jacobs on mouth harp; and installed both Johnny Dankworth and Alexis Korner as residents at the Marquee. I think my little visit was a year too early for Korner's regular nights with Blues Incorporated and the birth of the Stones, who played their first-ever gig under that name there in July 1962. But my night at the Marquee was like peeking through a heavy drape to another gloriously colourful planet.

My mental picture of that night starts with the trip down the basement stairs to the girl behind the desk outside the club door. As though my brain was switched on at the street-level entrance, all before that walk down those stairs is blank. The whole time I was thinking, why is it possible I'm here? I'm only a kid, how have they got me in? Of course, I now know that the Marquee, like so many of the innovative joints of the decade, was unlicensed. I was a gawky lanky thirteen year old, and not quite as out of place as I felt, it seemed.

The image that struck me the hardest was that of Ottilie Patterson. When she did her numbers they bathed her in a subdued blue light. The colours were an awesome part of the whole experience for me, and added to this marvellous woman delivering her sex-charged blues . . . I felt 'let in' to an adult world; this was no Chipperfield's Circus and its bloody clowns, this was sex on wheels, and Hello, world.

I came away from the Marquee with a taste for the blues, female singers, basement stairs. I read the *Melody Maker* every week now too, while my mates would bring in the flimsy bedraggled *New Musical Express* to school. Not that this was a bad thing; the *NME* had the serious pop news, the all-important pictures of Cliff and Elvis. I just didn't need to buy it because they did, and I had my *MM*. Sometimes it seemed pretty square, but let me say this: *Melody Maker* was raving about Ray Charles right next to Acker Bilk. And because of the paper's allegiance to jazz and dance bands it had the all-important back pages: some dedicated to instruments for sale, which would be meaningful to me less than a year later; also listings of clubs, to which I could dream of returning; the musicians who were the backbone of British jazz, and . . . classifieds that one day would feature the guy who would advisedly not be a 'bread head.' You know, 'Guitarist wanted, must have own gear, clean licence, contract waiting, no bread heads.'

Seeing Chris Barber and his band had an influence on my becoming a musician. We went and saw them again, this time at Croydon Civic Hall – not so romantic a venue, but I did get to sport a straw boater I'd acquired from somewhere, and got a few looks. Hello, vanity. It would be about another four years before Dad took me to see Woody Herman, twice, I think, and Buddy Rich, definitely twice; Fairfield Hall in Croydon both times. It was because Rich was a drummer, as was I by then. I thought he displayed fantastic trickery but was too much of a circus act for me. I was a Gene Krupa man. I enjoyed a good solid swinging beat, even if Krupa's technique was beyond me. Dad and I saw Duke Ellington at Fairfield Hall, 17 February 1965. Maybe the last thing we saw together. Fabulous is the true word for that, and even at the time I knew it was a special honour to be witnessing this swinging band that included Harry Carnie, Sam Woodyard, Johnny Hodges and Cooty Williams. I can still remember the Duke's wonderful voice and his familiar signing off: 'We do love you madly.'

If I may be allowed one more quote from the Duke, I like his response to a missed award one year. 'Fate is being kind to me. Fate doesn't want me to be famous too young.' He could have been speaking for me.

So You Wanna Be a Rock 'n' Roll Star

In October 1962 the New Addington Red Cross put on the first Rock & Twist Festival at the Community Centre. Six rock groups, mainly local bands, took part in the competition while competitors from the crowd, vying for cash prizes for the best dancing couples, showed off the latest crazes – the madison, the twist and the locomotion. During the intervals, music was supplied by the Partners. In the Croydon area, and sprawling out across the south-west London suburbs, we were spoilt for rock groups, and the local dance halls in which to see them. The competing groups this night were the Astronauts, the Alpines, the Deputies (who included local boy Matt Fisher, later of Procol Harum, and in front of whom I would one day audition– a miserable experience), the Emeralds, the Firebugs and the Vampires (who wore grotesque devil-like masks and black capes). Judged by volume of applause, Acton group the Firebugs won the first prize of £5 followed by the Emeralds with £3 and the Deputies with £2.

At this point I had been teaching myself to play drums for about three months. Having formed a group with classmates from school, and spent several weeks agonising over names, costumes and tunes, at the eleventh hour the boy picked to be our drummer decided he was switching to guitar. For me, the idea of being in a group was more important than the instrument I played, so I switched to drums. The guitar catalogues I had sent for by post, and lusted and planned over for weeks, got stashed. There was one almighty row with my parents over my desire to be a drummer. However, as one of them had mentioned noise and the neighbours, I came up with an answer. 'Okay, I'll go for trumpet then.' This may have worked on a sympathy level, at least with Mum. They, or at least she, gave in to the idea of the drums.

The summer break that followed the capitulation of my parents I spent fathoming an ancient tutor book, playing along to Joe Meek instrumentals with my sticks on a plastic washing bowl donated by Mum, and beating biscuit tins over at Grandma's house accompanying her music-hall singing and piano styling. Upon returning to school after the summer break, not one of my new group had done anything about furthering their musical career, including the ex-drummer who had been going to get a Watkins Rapier guitar from his dad. I stuck to drums, as I'd started learning now, and had fought my parents for the privilege.

At the Rock & Twist Festival that October I sat with Chris and his then girlfriend, Tina. Tina was lovely, with long, wavy strawberry blonde tresses. She had got into a bit of a rumble with another girl who Chris had been going out with before. This was typical of the kind of trouble Chris was already instigating by being quite forward in the pursuit of the opposite sex. In less than a year the Rolling Stones would make themselves known and Chris's uncanny similarity to their frontman (albeit younger and prettier!) would attract even more of the same trouble. We were all between fourteen and fifteen, and as innocent as the day is long. During the show, I was enthralled in equal parts by the look and sound of live rock 'n' roll, and Tina's knees. I didn't know then that Tina would be *my* girlfriend in the not too distant future.

That Christmas I got my first kit. A snare drum and hi-hat were all my parents could afford, so that's how I started. I had given up on my first group ever coming to anything. On the first day back at school after the break, I was approached in the playground, before we got whistled into line, by Dave James. Dave had made a name for himself as the school pop star. He was often seen carrying a guitar into school, and during one school choir session, he was asked by our music teacher, with misplaced politeness, if he'd mind singing a verse (as if it might hurt his voice)! Dave had achieved his reputation by being a supreme bullshitter. He was like a cross between Walter Mitty and Peer Gynt. We had always been friendly, although not in the same school form, and now, somehow, he had already discovered I was the owner of a drum kit. From that day on the two of us tried to form a group.

Our first performance was accompanying a relief music and art teacher who had an experimental idea. This serious young man also played a deft boogie-woogie piano, and his idea was to set a handful of hymns to a boogie-woogie rhythm, with himself on piano, me on drums and Dave playing his guitar through the music room gramophone speaker. The music class was a set of rather serious fifth-year boys who were made to sing the hymns to our accompaniment and, for reasons I could not fathom, unanimously hated the experience. Obviously it had been an early attempt by a student teacher to engage boys normally bored by classical music lessons, but they failed to respond with anything but contempt. I was bemused by their inability to grasp that they were on to a good thing. My first performance before my contemporaries, and a failure. And Dave blew up the school speaker, so we weren't asked again.

Meanwhile, throughout the school, word had spread about my drumming. Another of the younger, but more permanent, teachers had been a jitterbug champion in his not-too-long-ago youth. He also fancied himself as a bit of a singer. On a prearranged afternoon I took my little kit down to his form room, where I accompanied the teacher as he sang and played 'Peggy Sue' on a guitar. I had been practising the drum pattern from Buddy Holly's record on my snare for weeks, and my left hand was still failing me towards the end of the song. Mind you, this teacher was using his own form as his audience, giving them a treat, and they loved him for it. So the first rock 'n' roll song I ever played before an audience was 'Peggy Sue'.

My first professional 'gig' was in the mud of a wet field somewhere on a pig farm in Kent, at the Saltbox Motorcycle Club's annual picnic and barbecue. We were a three-piece – Dave, another Brian on bass, and me. The amplification surrendered to the bad earthing that also gave Dave a shock or two before a helpful biker placed an engineer's boot on the mains supply in one of the pig sheds. The huge roaring bonfire put the guitar strings out of tune, and we ended up performing most of the gig with Dave singing and playing a borrowed acoustic guitar and me beating a snare drum and hi-hat that were sinking in the mud. After all this we actually got paid, and I had made my first public appearance. Dave told me we had replaced a renegade Gene Vincent and the Outlaws who had been booked to play the gig. I still like to believe that.

Dave was an incorrigible liar. He also had a way of appropriating other people's names. In that first year of trying to form a group with Dave we entered the New Addington Red Cross Rock & Twist Contest held in October 1963. Dave borrowed two guys, the bass and rhythm guitar from a fairly successful local rock group called the Blue Rangers. Then he entered this one-off four-piece combo into the talent contest under the name Syndicate One. Quite a good name, I thought, until I spotted an ad in the back of *Melody Maker* placed by a group called Syndicate One, from up north. We didn't get anywhere in the talent contest, so never had a problem with the 'other' group, but it must be said, the other guys in our group would probably have done much better just entering as the Blue Rangers.

The bogus Syndicate One happened to be competing at the contest against a very interesting young group from the Thornton Heath area called the Nesters, basically a family outfit. The lead guitarist and singer was a handsome guy called Glen, and his little sister, about fifteen years old, if that, played drums and sang, both extremely well. They were what was known then as Anglo-Indian, and consequently the possessors of jet-black hair and great looks. Chris was with me that night, along with my parents. Once the Nesters started their set Chris could not keep his eyes off Holly, the girl drummer, and he chatted her up as soon as they had finished their set. The Nesters fared as badly as we did in that contest, though they really deserved to do well.

By the end of 1963 Dave and I had formed the Classics, which comprised me, Dave, a bass player called Tony Perry and a pudgy rhythm guitarist with the wonderful rock 'n' roll name of Nicky Holley. The search for a bass player was by far our most time-consuming activity. When we heard that Tony, who lived just along the road from me, had a guitar of some sort, we called over with the express purpose of convincing him he should get a bass. Which meant that he would have to convince his mum to get him a bass. Which he did!

Within no time Tony was the owner of a brand new Framus violin bass. The Framus was a copy of the Hofner violin bass that Paul McCartney was using in a beat combo that had started making waves around this time. Upon hearing that Tony had the bass, Dave needed to find out how he was progressing. So round to Tony's house we went once more. On this occasion Dave asked Tony to play the bass riff from 'I Wanna Be Your Man', recently released by the Rolling Stones. This Bill Wyman riff is basically a cool but finger-twisting twelve-bar riff that takes more stamina than talent to emulate. It was then known as the 'never get your knickers twisted' riff. Tony seemed to have mastered it, and Dave announced he was in our band. The date of the Stones' hit makes the official formation of the Classics December 1963.

Nicky left us quite early on, and we became a trio. Then Mr Barker, our music teacher who was very supportive, asked us to give a little recital for one of his classes. As we were a guitar, bass and drums line-up, we tended towards covers of similar three-piece groups, like the Big Three and the Pirates. I know we definitely played a version of Bo Diddley's 'I Can Tell' *à la* the Pirates. Unfortunately, our headmaster's office was opposite the music room across a square of green, meaning he heard every note. Mr Barker was summarily informed that no such performance could be allowed again. So much for the school system's sympathy for rock 'n' roll. After this, our long-suffering music master allowed Dave and I to 'rehearse' in a closet along the corridor from the music room. We did so for quite some time, but wastefully spent most of the time playing avant-garde improvisation for guitar and snare drum instead of working out tunes.

I Was in Love with Christine Keeler

There were some other rather important events taking place in England during this time. And they played their part in impressing me as much as any other baby boomer. During the same summer that I was taken to the Marquee, a pretty girl from the Home Counties called Christine Keeler was having an affair with the Conservative Secretary of State for War, John Profumo, and simultaneously bedding Russian naval attaché Eugene Ivanov. At pretty much the same time West Indian émigré musician Johnny Edgecombe was running an illegal drinking club in the worn-down west London area of Ladbroke Grove – it was, in the Sunday paper parlance of the time, 'a drink and drugs den' in Notting Hill. A fellow West Indian known as Lucky Gordon, who frequented Johnny's shebeen, threatened to squeal on Johnny to the police about the club. Johnny closed the shebeen and moved into the jazz world, where he became a driver and dope dealer.

In September of that year Johnny met Christine, who was working as a nightclub hostess in the legitimate gentlemen's club world up town, and moved into her flat. For a while Johnny tolerated Christine's wayward habits, until the day she told him that Lucky Gordon had assaulted her and held her captive after she had ended a tryst with him. In October Johnny attacked Lucky outside the Flamingo Jazz Club in Wardour Street and left Lucky unluckily needing seventeen stitches in his face.

In December Johnny Edgecombe's arrest for firing shots at the door of a flat where Christine was hiding would unravel a scandal just waiting to bubble to the surface.

In October of 1962, Radio Luxembourg played, for the first time anywhere, a record called 'Love Me Do'. I heard that first broadcast, believe it or not, and I cannot say the experience lived up to what I remember the DJ promising. As the big sound at the time was dominated by girl groups from New York, and *our* groups tended to be instrumental and twangy, I assumed it was an American group, because they sang. I didn't think they measured up to the Shangri-Las, the Dixie Cups or the Cookies.

Also that month London experienced its last great smog, a real pea-souper, before the Clean Air Act came into force. It nevertheless introduced a winter that no-one saw coming. The winter of 1962–63 would become known as the Big Freeze. BBC news expressed the fear that the Strait of Dover might freeze over. The upper reaches of the Thames did freeze over, though not in central London, partly due to the hot effluent from the two thermal power stations at Battersea and Bankside. People were, however, skating on parts of the river. I remember there was a snow fall as late as June.

January saw the release of 'Please Please Me' by the Fab Four. By the last day of the month it had entered some charts straight in at number seventeen. As I listened to some of the earliest reports of Beatlemania on the radio at Grandma's house during the last days of the Christmas break, I watched the next-door neighbour's lean-to roof collapse as the snow fell to the ground, taking the old roofing with it.

That March Johnny Edgecombe's case came up at the Old Bailey, which broke the story open, and in June the trial of the unfortunate scapegoat, Stephen Ward, led to the downfall of Profumo, who resigned his post. In August 1963 Stephen Ward killed himself on the morning of his sentencing. His suicide was a mirror of another high-profile suicide that would take place four years later, relating to the Moptops who were at the top of the charts at the time and would be for the rest of the decade.

All during this time my fifteen-year-old mind was fed these wonders from the *News of the World* that landed in our midst every Sunday. For reasons I could never fathom, my father took the *Daily Telegraph* during the week, then relaxed at the weekend and enjoyed truffling in the shit with the rest of the nation. The Profumo affair filled me with mental pictures of Notting Hill marijuana dens, the effect of that exotic sweet foreign aroma on cream-skinned English call girls, the dangerous West Indians who ran the walk-in clubs that my anti-heroine scored at in Westbourne Grove, the procurers of sex, drugs and kinks to people in high places, of wild parties at stately homes and low dungeons, all starring people from a class we thought we'd never join. It all fuelled my fevered furtive imagination out there in my suburban hinterland.

I was infatuated with Christine, the dangerous brunette. As for the rest, I couldn't have known then, I would live it all eventually, and in the same manor I was reading about in the *News of the World*!

Where Did Our Love Go?

In September 1963 it was Tina's birthday. She had moved away from New Addington and was now living and attending her last school in Streatham in south London. I wrote her a birthday card, which led to letters, and finally to my travelling to that south London suburb and my first love affair. Our romance was so, so innocent. Tina was someone I took two buses to go and see, and my parents must have thought, how sweet. She even came to our house and went to some of my gigs, even to a dinner dance of Mum's. But to our parents we were still children, and our little scene together was no threat to the status quo.

On 22 November an assassin spectacularly took the life of President John F. Kennedy in Dallas. Anyone old enough can remember the TV screens going black. It was a moment that involved us all. I got a letter from Tina and one of the things she wrote was, 'Wasn't it terrible about Kennedy?' Funny what you remember, isn't it?

Just as I turned sixteen I met Kathy. Kathy was different. Kathy was my first real girlfriend. She lived on the estate, not far from us. She had bags of attitude. Dad had said to me on more than one occasion, 'As soon as you get a girlfriend, son, your mother's not going to like it.' And here came Kathy. What may have made things hard for both my folks, was that it was so very obvious that the kid was learning his carnal knowledge at the college of Kathy. When we all went in our car on picnics out to the country, Kathy and I would be really busy under a blanket in the back seat to and from our destination. How could they not know?

We had begun to take many of these motor outings with Fred and his family, in two cars. Mum had met Fred as part of a foil fencing group she had joined. A couple of years earlier Mum had tried to get me interested in fencing, and we had started classes together. I lasted less than a year – it was, after all, sport, and I had never taken the slightest interest in any kind of sport at school or outside. Football represented for me being yelled at and called a girl by some frustrated physical education master while standing around in the snow, wind and mud – in shorts! Mum continued with the fencing, and met some people she would stay friends with from then on. One of them was Fred. But he was more than a friend. I first met Fred when I was fifteen, or I should say Dad and I first met him then – he and Mum had known each other for some time already. For some years to follow my mother managed a balancing act, as she conducted an affair of the heart while keeping up her righteous nagging of me. And she kept up a cold front towards poor young Kathy, as she would for each and every girlfriend I would have for the rest of my life. Just as Dad had said she would.

Kathy and I had got started at a party at Classics bassist Tony Perry's house just after my sixteenth birthday in 1964. She'd planned it. Meeting me, not the party. My mate Alan Young, another school friend I'd hung out with a lot, had emigrated on the old £10 ticket with his family to New Zealand, and left his girl behind. Now she was looking for me. The Classics played at the party that night. Kathy was my first serious girlfriend and she took my virginity, bless her. Not at the party, a bit later. At the party she gave me my first serious kiss.

* * *

49

Our three-piece group was extended a little later in the year. There were two very young fellows who frequented the local youth clubs who called themselves the Micatones because their names were Tony Martin and Mick Fuller. See what they did there? Tony strummed an acoustic guitar and they sang in close Everly Brothers-style harmonies, at the same time choosing some tunes popular with the Mersey Sound, like 'Money'. Their close harmonies were very good.

One day Dave told me that the Micatones were joining the Classics. So now we had two singers, plus Dave, Tony and me, and we had also found another rhythm guitarist called Richard. One of the first gigs we played was at a function for the Electricity Board, where my aunty worked. So there we were, all six of us, wearing leather jackets and playing our repertoire of Jimmy Reed twelve-bar blues mixed with some Chuck Berry.

One of the Micatones had a habit of blowing up a Durex and tying it to the headstock of one of the guitars. As if this was not enough for the workforce of my aunty's company, I had invited along Kathy, and of course all my family were there. After all, the kid's group is playing for aunty's firm's do. Brashly, during the break Kathy and I sat in a corner snogging, and I got myself a face full of red lipstick into the bargain. This did not sit too well with Mum, or anyone else in the family for that matter. My parents both showed acute embarrassment for my aunty's colleagues and ticked me off in front of my group. It wasn't my best behaviour, to be honest.

The group went down very well, however. People in those days used to say, 'You're as good as/not quite as good as the Beatles.' Of course, we were nothing like them.

One day, quite suddenly, Dave upped and left the Classics. We had a booking at some school hall which we needed to honour, so Richard switched to lead guitar and the Micatones had to pull off a whole gig with their repertoire. It was a hall with a high stage, and for some reason there was a row of people in wheelchairs down by the front. It brought to mind the Beatles and their renowned healing power. Tony and Mick ran out of songs quite early on and, much to everyone's amazement, launched into a ventriloquist act! Mick, the smaller of the two, sat on Tony's knee, and they went through an old 'gottle of geer' routine.

Rock 'n' roll!

* * *

During this time Chris had continued to chase Holly, the little drummer girl. He had found out that the Nesters rehearsed in a pub in south Croydon, and that they invited friends in to their rehearsals for the entrance fee of a shilling. They would set chairs up in the rented room like a gig and basically run through their set. I remember the Nesters did great versions of the Stones' 'Tell Me' and Eddie Cochran's 'Nervous Breakdown'. Any new songs they would have worked up at home. Chris asked me to go along with him, and so I took Kathy, and we made it a fairly regular thing for a while. The idea was that during the set I would sit in for a couple of numbers, so that Chris could chat up Holly.

Chris was outrageous. It became obvious pretty quickly that Holly was very young, came from a strict Catholic family, her older brother was watching over her, and she was *going out with the bass player* . . . and yet while I rocked through a couple of tunes Chris sat with Holly, bold as brass, with his arm around her! Well, we got away with those shenanigans at the time, but soon the rehearsals seemed to disappear, together with Holly.

* * *

One day I was helping my mother, begrudgingly, do the washing up. She was uptight about something, and we soon fell into one of our customary bickerings. She was nagging me, about what is lost in the mists of time, and my temper, as was always the case, rose to the bait. I really lost it this time, freaked out and smashed the wet crockery against the kitchen wall, both of us screaming at the top of our lungs. She then, turning away from me, started praying for God's forgiveness for *begetting* me! At this I was dumbfounded and more than a little embarrassed. When she had regained her composure she told me I had to give up Kathy, my lovelife not having cropped up in the argument till then, showing she believed my bad behaviour was due to my relationship with my girlfriend, rather than with her, which was the truth. I didn't do as I was told.

Chris and I were in the fifth year, doing GCEs, which involved attending some evening classes. As I needed time to see Kathy, I skipped some of these. We hung out with nowhere to go. I felt sorry for her having to go out with a guy whose mother had forbidden her son to see her. Chris and I also bunked off during the day sometimes. On one of these occasions the three of us were round at my maisonette. Kathy and I were in my single bed, Chris was clattering away at my old typewriter in the lounge, the name we gave the sitting room at home. We both fancied ourselves as writers, and were both writing books. For some reason I climbed out of bed and peeped out of the window, just in time to see Mum pull up in her funky little Morris. God knows why she was arriving home at this time in the afternoon. With hindsight, I have a feeling she was as embarrassed to be caught out coming home at that time as we were freaked out by her arrival.

We leapt into action. Kathy grabbed her clothes and hid under the bed as I opened the door to warn Chris. He had also got a weird feeling, and had looked out of the lounge window, seeing my mum himself. He was standing in the doorway as I opened it, stark naked. I was saying, 'My mum!' At the same time Chris was shouting in my face, 'Your mum!' I told him to keep her busy and rushed into the bathroom with my clothes. So while I was pretending to be answering nature's call, and pulling on my clothes double-fast, Chris engaged Mum in the kitchen in a conversation about Germany, from where she had just returned. (Her trips to Germany at this time proved to have something to do with her burgeoning affair with Fred.) I emerged from the bathroom, said hello, explained how we had taken some time out from school – no explanation was forthcoming from her about her being home early – and sidled back into my bedroom.

Kathy was still under the bed. Mum came in and started talking about nothing in particular. Was she trying to act cool herself? I spied a stray bra among the bedding and whipped it under the covers as I pretended to straighten out the bed. Did she see it? Soon she went back to the kitchen and I slung the bra down under the bed, telling Kathy to be ready to split. I then walked coolly into the kitchen and grabbed the waste bin. Out of the kitchen, back into my bedroom, I told Kathy to follow me fast, and we both legged it out the door. As I emptied the rubbish into the dustbin I told her I'd see her later, as I planned to skip evening classes that night.

I should stress that this misadventure illustrates one of the reasons I did spectacularly badly in my GCEs. I had stayed for a fifth year, as had Chris, in order to take O levels. At secondary modern school it was not compulsory to stay past the fourth year, or to take any leaving exams. I was a good student, but a lazy one. And I was distracted by many things, sex most definitely being one of them. Already I had been denied the chance to take any of the sciences because of underachievement through the year, and I ended up sitting about five subjects. I passed only two: technical drawing, in which I excelled, and English language – the subject for which I had been the poster boy of my year throughout school, but I barely limped through. Once again, my chance of going on to college was thwarted. My parents were disappointed and

53

showed it. It turned out I did not even sit enough papers to have got a place in a college, even if I'd passed them all. The school did offer a sixth year, for those wanting to try again or to try for more – the equivalent of staying on for A levels at a grammar school. I had already decided to leave that summer, without yet even knowing my shocking results. I should have stayed on, especially considering the life of ho-hum jobs that waited for me round the corner. As for my parents, it was the eleven-plus all over again. This time they gave up on me.

Chris stayed on for the sixth form, a decision made for him by his mother. One day she just went into the school and made the arrangements without his knowing. He lasted until the following Easter, and then left anyway.

With the pressure of exams that we were not passing, and our failure to please our parents at every turn, Chris and I did not discuss our problems. Like all of us at the time, we felt our problems were ours alone. Chris told me years later that he started reading upon leaving school, and later even took some subjects he was interested in at O level. For us, our education started after school was out.

When Kathy and I split up, her mother chased me all over the estate; she wanted to have a word. She then got my parents round when I proved to be too elusive, with my knowledge of the back alleys. When I arrived back home, I found Mum and Dad back there before me, but they had had a little visit with Kathy's folks. Ironic, I always thought, that they all met up after we'd split. Mum was unusually quiet, and Dad was full of hot air. They'd been shown my letters to Kathy, and his marvellous piece of philosophy for me was, 'You're sixteen. What do you know about love?'

Pirates

Easter 1964 Chris came round and knocked on my front door during the school break. The first thing he said was, had I been listening to the radio? Easter Sunday 1964 was the first day of Radio Caroline, the very first pirate radio station to open for business, broadcasting full-time. It had been available for two or three days by the time we tuned in the radiogram – and there it was.

From a world of *Two Way Family Favourites*, *Easy Beat*, *Friday Night is Music Night*, military tattoos, sleepy folk ballads, through the years of kneeling in front of the family radiogram, twisting the tuner oh so gently, bending the ear for Radio Luxembourg, Fab 208 . . . to THIS! Suddenly a world of twenty-four hour pop music, DELIVERY. No more waiting for a pearl among the dross. Wow, this was like America (as we thought of it). This was one of the defining moments ushering in the sixties. From this moment on, the soundtrack to our lives would be a Detroit handclap with a tambourine on the backbeat. A hundred memorable Tamla melodies, 'flashbacks' keeping the fifties alive, new sounds Aunty Beeb would not dare to play. 'Sureshots', the sides the pirate jocks were paid to play, the mid-Atlantic accent. From 'Not Fade Away' by the Rolling Stones via the Chirping Crickets, all the way to Radio London (I had the T-shirt) playing 'A Day in the Life' on 14 August 1967 when the government's new law, the Marine Broadcasting Offences Act of 1967, came into force and closed down all the pirates – Radio London, Radio Britain, *et al* – except for Caroline. And she went off the air one day in March 1968, when I was at my current girlfriend's parents' house listening and thinking about the few years that had passed since they had started it all.

Factory Estate (Know Your Place)

Having spent the summer of 1964 waiting to hear the results of my GCEs, and then learning the desperate reality, I went for a job interview around September, on the factory estate near where I lived, Vulcan Way. Warner Glass was a glazing firm that made and fitted metal windows, roof lights, curtain walling, that sort of thing. They were looking for an estimating clerk. Now I never saw myself as any kind of clerk, but the work involved reading drawings in order to estimate the amount of glass required. In that way it utilised the one subject I had excelled in with O levels: technical drawing. I was interviewed by two men. They asked me how much I expected to be paid, and I said I didn't know, this was my first job. One of them said, how about £4 a week? I said that sounds fine, even though it did sound low even for then, even for a beginner. When I said that, the man who had asked me gave his colleague a funny look, a half smirk. I smelled a rat but it was too late. I had had the piss taken out of me.

So, for my first job I was paid £4 per week, and I gave Mum £1 of it. For perspective, a pint of Double Diamond or Watneys Red Barrel was a shilling, single records were six shillings and seven pence, and bus fares were measured in pennies. But that doesn't mean £4 was a lot of money – the average weekly wage was £16, and I suppose a kid starting out should have expected to be paid £7 or £8.

I sat at a desk next to my boss, whose name was Eric. In the estimating department there were five people. Across the desk was George, who was in charge of metal windows, and he had two assistants. On my side there were just Eric and me. Eric was a cunt. He would have been a cunt with anyone who had been sent to work with him. From the outset Eric would treat me as if I was an idiot, and he acted exasperated at the slightest little thing he could think of to pick on me about. It was browbeating, and it was consistent. Now George seemed to be a lovely, eccentric little man who wore a bow tie, hummed little tunes, and whose assistants seemed to have no bother with him. I deserved to work with George, I deserved to start my working life with a kind, happy-go-lucky chap like George, but I got lumbered with Eric. I struck shit. Eric's favourite expression was, 'Don't joke!' I wasn't joking, Eric.

This job could have led on to better things. It was clean, it involved using the brain, it was a sort of 'Mod' job, and I might have gone on to do more if I had stayed. But I couldn't last longer than six months with Eric, and that was that.

One of George's two assistants was a guy called Pete, a year older than me, and a Mod. I was at the beginning of my Rocker phase, but we got on really well and he would bring in records for me to borrow. He was in love with Marianne Faithfull. Outside of Pete's acts of kindness, we had no discussions about our cultural choices. That is, we didn't talk about Mods and Rockers. Looking back I should have asked Pete round to my house, or got invited over to his, but I was too hung up on my own scene. I did not make new friends easily.

Right next door to Warner Glass was Unichem, the major pharmaceutical manufacturer and supplier of drugs and medicine to the whole country. The branch on Vulcan Way may have covered London, or maybe further afield, I have no idea. But the irony was that Kathy had taken a job there, and I don't know what she was employed as, but I do know that some of her colleagues supplied the West End with French blues.

'Blues', 'uppers', or 'leapers' had taken over from Purple Hearts, which were the drinamyl tablets that had caught the attention of the *News of the World*. Kathy was by now a top 'blocking' Mod. Being 'blocked' was the term used by pill-heads to denote being high on pills. The Block was also a dance, which Kathy once demonstrated to my family when we were round at Grandma's. We were like Eddie and Sheena, but about fifteen years too early. Sometimes we met outside after work and chatted, me feeling a sweet and sour mixture of loss and poignancy. We never got back together; we didn't want that exactly.

Whenever I hear 'My Guy' by Mary Wells I think of Kathy.

After I expressed dissatisfaction with the job at Warner Glass, Dad said, 'You're always reading those *Hot Rod* magazines, why don't you get a job as a motor mechanic? Learn a trade, you should learn a trade.' Gawd, I was about to fall so low. A grease monkey! I knew it would be nothing like the magazines, but I was desperate. I didn't want to do *anything*, I knew that. But Dad sent me off in the wrong direction anyway. Someone in the family knew someone in management at Leathwoods, a garage in Selhurst, south London.

* * *

Why was I not a Mod? I think it had something to do with living in the suburbs, although quite a few of my school contemporaries turned into Mods, especially from the year behind us. I was aware of the changing style, the new Italian cut, and I've mentioned the points and the chisel toes. If any youth could be bothered to spend time on his barnet then that was a sign. I had been teasing my tresses into an Elvis clone since the last year at Juniors, while the popular style by now among even the hardnuts was a flatter top with a minimal wave in front. I think the Shadows, especially Jet Harris and Tony Meehan, had the modern style down cold.

When the Beatles came along they looked a real oddity. But for the teens who hadn't followed any style till then, it seemed as if the world had morphed into moptops after being Elvis just last week. Besides, as soon as that idea was established, along came the Stones, not to mention the Pretty Things, another band playing rough-and-ready rhythm and blues, both bands sporting unbelievable and impressive hursuitness – especially the Pretties, whose records were tougher too. Chris, in the face of contemporary ridicule, had been growing his hair and dumping the Brilliantine long before this.

I always felt that the Mods and Rockers were a bit like Cavaliers and Roundheads. With the Rockers being the Cavaliers, having the adventurous spirit, the sense of honour, the fight-to-the-death attitude, a conservative outlook and, of course, being royalists. Mods were like Roundheads because they represented the 'new way', were more like republicans, were loyal only to the precepts of their parliament, tended to group in huge numbers, and also appeared to outsiders to look alike. Of course, my theory falls apart if the Mods' dandyish attitude to sartorial detail is taken into consideration, and it also only holds true of the latter-day scooter brigade, not the original Modernists.

Hair. I saw some wonderful 'do's' on the estate, many of them 'out of time'. One guy who got off the bus at my stop, an older guy who lived nearby, had a 'silver dollar' to die for. The sides were slicked back to a perfect DA (duck's arse), not long and greasy, but well-trimmed, the meeting at the back ruler sharp. On top was a perfect flat-top with a neat wave at the front about an inch high. I never saw anyone else with a style like it. Then there were two Teds getting on the bus once, who sat in front of me on the top. They had totally matching hair. The front was in a bunch of grapes (a group of tight curls), possibly permed, the sides straight and meeting at the back in the perfect DA, but then at the nape of the neck was *another* bunch of grapes! And the two of them were dressed alike too. This was well after the Edwardian vogue, although one could still spy many very smart Teds around Croydon long after the event. The memory of those two Teds reminds me of the first time I saw desert boots. Again on the top of a bus, but this time two well-suited Mods. On their feet were brand new Clarks blond numbers, and they blew my mind. I had to have some. I was already working out how they would fit in with my Rocker image.

By the time Chris and I had decided to go the Rocker route, late in the summer of '64, the Mod thing had already peaked by London standards. Out Croydon way, the Mods were dedicated followers. The few with a taste for the real Mod life had vanished across the River, instead spending their time up in Soho, where many of the sleazier clubs' doormen would be the Teds who had left school four years before them. Among the Mod advance guard would be the guys who eventually took the road to Amsterdam, then India or Afghanistan. Many of us would meet somewhere along the way.

I only went to the coast once during that 'Mods and Rockers battle' invention. The tabloids came up with the term 'Mods and Rockers'. They had discovered Mods at a time when the original Modernists were getting concerned that the exclusivity was disappearing from their scene, and with the attendant mass-production of 'Mod'-style clothes in Carnaby Street. Since the tabloids needed to stress a tribal angle, they found that out in the sticks there was still a healthy surviving 'ton-up boy' scene. Young men who rode powerful motorbikes had become known as ton-up boys after their supposed desire to occasionally take their machines up to the magical hundred miles per hour and over. They labelled these people 'Rockers', in a kind of reference to their seemingly fifties styling. Nobody was called a Rocker before the first tabloid article. It was when you read the article that you thought, 'Right, if I'm not a Mod, I must be a Rocker.' Add to this that bikers always went on bank holiday runs, usually to the coast. If you have two wheels and there are a few of you, you need to go on a run. It's the same the world over. So when the Mods started riding scooters, and there were enough of them, they did the same thing as the Rockers. The first place they clashed, according to legend, was Margate. I went to Brighton incognito – that is to say, not looking Rocker. From the car window the scene was amazing, but not in a good way. You always see those same old scenes of Mods running along streets, jumping over walls at the promenade, fighting, being arrested. But the reality at Brighton on the day I went in 1964 was wall-to-wall parkas. The streets were rammed shoulder to shoulder with boys and girls all looking the same and doing nothing. Even as somebody not involved with Mod, it was obvious that this was the end. This display of uniformity, this vast army of parka-clad clones, was the death knell of something that could only ever be sustained by a select and discreet few. You cannot sustain a scene where the comparison of cloth is paramount to your conversation in a world of thousands of similarly clad people. Perhaps you cannot dance a new dance on a dance floor where no-one can see you. It was over, and thus sayeth the true faces at the time.

Rockers

New Addington needed its fair share of youth clubs, owing to the dearth of any entertainment generally on the estate. Some of the clubs were church-run, while others were independent. What they had in common was that they played records, kids danced, there was no real lower age limit, there was Coke for sale, and there was table tennis. That's probably about it, unless my memory is failing me. Chris and I used to frequent the Goldcrest as our club of choice.

It was on one of our visits to the Goldcrest – it must have been mid-'64 – that the club held a fancy dress night. The rule was you didn't have to wear fancy dress to get in, but it would be nice if you made the effort. We didn't. So we were lounging around in there when Pete Bruce made an entrance. Pete had attended Overbury School, but had left before we did and used to, for some reason, hang around our school gates on a push bike waiting for us. He had also been present at the party at Tony Perry's house earlier that year, where I'd met Kathy. This night he was wearing ice-blue jeans, pointy black boots, a leather jacket that had 'Pete – A Hells Angel' on the back. All topped off with a customised conductor's cap that was bedecked with chains and studs. Apparently he had been stopped at the door and told, 'No leather jackets allowed.' His reply had been, 'I'm in fancy dress,' and he was allowed in. He spent the evening doing a slow version of the twist, and by slow I mean he was deliberately twisting at half the tempo of the records. The rest of the time he was doing a version of 'Ringo's

Dog', as demonstrated in *A Hard Day's Night*, which looks like the dancer is sparring with his partner. At least the way Pete did it with his mates, it looked like sparring. Chris and I looked on, amused. This was our clarion call to the world of Rockers. Within no time Chris and I were dressed like Pete.

Once you were a Rocker there were certain places you hung out. At the southern end of the estate the only exit road was a narrow lane that led through the Kent countryside. Three miles directly south, as this road curved through sharp doglegs cutting through the very woods we had been made to splash along for school cross-country runs, you got to Saltbox Hill. At the top of Saltbox Hill you met the Westerham Road at an impossible angle. Walking to the top of Saltbox Hill was hard, but driving up onto the Westerham Road took honed clutch skills in car or on bike. Just to the right, lying under the lip of the main road, was the Saltbox Café.

When we were still at school we had hung out at the Saltbox. As far back as 1961 I remember spending a lot of change playing U.S. Bonds' 'Quarter To Three' over and over on the jukebox, and getting glowering stares from lorry drivers. One summer I watched as Billy Fury and Dickie Pride, the former a pop star at the top of his game, the latter a great little performer who never made it far out of infamous pop impresario Larry Parnes' much-touted 'stable', drew up in a two-seater sports car. Billy had bought a house in the exclusive enclave of Shirley Hills and Dickie was a local boy-made-by-Parnes from Monks Hill estate, and they hung out together. I was told by more than a couple of reliable sources that later on they did LSD together. But that would be another time and place for all of us. So, Billy and Dickie climbed over the doors of the two-seater and they were both wearing tight leather gaucho pants with rosettes and tassels all up the sides. Absolute rock 'n' roll cool.

There were two other cafés along the Westerham Road. If you

turned left (east) from the crest of Saltbox Hill you came to the main entrance to Biggin Hill Aerodrome. The aerodrome is the reason for the cafés along the Westerham Road. Biggin Hill was the airstrip from which the Spitfires of the Second World War would take off and to which, it was hoped, they would return. One of these machines sits permanently and proudly at the gates of the airfield next to a Hurricane. And of course, every year there was the Air Show, which most of us in New Addington could benefit from without going up to Biggin Hill. Opposite the entrance, more or less, was a café called the Squadron. To us Rockers the Squadron never quite made it, it seemed to lack any pazazz. The scene in *American Graffiti* where Curt walks into an empty amusement joint with the Pharaohs, intent on robbing the slots, reminds me of the Squadron. At the other end of the airfield you would get to the Nightingale Café, an even more popular café with the Rockers. By the time we started our Rocker career at the Saltbox, the Nightingale already had a 'hard' reputation that put Chris and me off. It was nevertheless far more the Rocker hang-out than the Saltbox, the clientele including a few older Teds and the juke box becoming famous for its fifties rock 'n' roll selection.

The late fifties/early sixties motorcycle riders became popularised as 'ton-up boys' before being lumbered with the tabloid name 'Rockers'. Ton-up boys were not the instigators of the café scene's bad reputation; nor, in fact, were they much involved in the later seaside rumbles with the much-maligned 'Mods' (really scooter boys). Police records indicated that many bikers ended up in casualty more often than not because of accidents on the way to or from certain cafés. Hence the police became aware of café racers. Facts suggested that café riders were accident prone, if not reckless, but didn't take into account the hangers-on. Among the bikers, it was alleged that the hangers-on were the less capable and therefore more accident-prone riders. Serious bikers often elicited favourable comment for their driving skills from police motorcyclists, who were reluctant to press charges. They also shared a love of their machines, of course.

It was at the famed Ace Café on the North Circular Road that, allegedly, someone had the idea of record racing, where a particular route had to be covered in the time it took a song to be played on the jukebox. Pop records were short, and the risks taken in the time the disc took to play often led to disaster. The record race was apparently popularised by an episode of the TV series *Dixon of Dock Green*, which was filmed at the Ace Café. It is said the record race was unknown in other areas prior to its screening.

Among the Nortons, Bonnevilles, Beezer Rockets and Goldies, all with *de rigueur* clip-on handlebars and racing seats, stood the riders, dressed in proper all-weather apparel, with not a stud in sight. We first appeared at the Saltbox wearing our Pete-influenced clothing, covered in studs and with our customised caps, which featured one important item, pinned right at the front: the skull and crossbones of the 17th/21st Lancers and their motto, 'Or Glory'. At the time there was only one place to get these treasured items; a military surplus shop on the Strand called Badges and Equipment. And in the meantime, we still hung out at the Goldcrest.

Chris and I showed up at the Goldcrest one night in 1964 in full Rocker drag, except I was wearing my new blue leather buckled P.J. Proby shoes (actually promoted as Tom Jones shoes, meaning the literary character played by Albert Finney in the film, rather than the singer). We were asking for trouble . . . and someone started it. There was a gang of them, and only two of us. One of the gang was a skinny, dour-looking chap with a dark drape jacket worn over jeans held up by a tan canvas army belt, the kind of belt you used to see around quite a lot still then.

The look did not suggest any kind of cool, merely hardness. We learned that the skinny guy was not long out of borstal. He turned out to be the one who did very little while bigger and thicker pals did a lot, mainly to impress him. We could have walked away, but I decided on the spur of the moment to use some karate moves I'd picked up from Elvis movies. Skinny guy got it in the throat, but as I mentioned, there were more behind him. I can remember seeing Chris valiantly attacking one of the rearguard as I was thrust head first into a wall. The wall was the end of the fracas. The resultant state of my head impressed even my assailants. Seemed like nobody was going to do anything about this incident – the gang were still there, we were still there, no figure of authority had come forward, and Chris and I felt sure the gang were going to meet us later, unless we disappeared quite fast. This we did, managing to slip out unseen, and hurrying along snow-covered streets through the estate. We did escape any further retribution, but I found it hard to convince my parents that the appalling damage done to my forehead was from walking into a door with a vicious return spring on it.

Not long after this incident, we turned up at the Hilltoppers, trying on a new bravery for size as we knew our recent 'combatants' frequented the club, and because Pete preferred the place. The Hilltoppers had a bad rep. Actually, the Hilltoppers wasn't all that bad really, or had been fairly trouble free in its beginnings. I had heard about it through most of secondary school, from mates, but I'd never gone. It was the first place most thirteen-year-olds locally got to hear and dance to pop records played over a loud speaker system. Little teenybopper girls could dance in socks, and little pre-teen guys could worry about spots. It was later, during the only times I visited the Hilltoppers, that the community centre where the club was held seemed to be peopled by older bored-looking blokes playing table tennis and giving newcomers filthy looks.

The gang who had done me in were there, and they interpreted our brazen visit as a show of bravado, which turned them into our new best friends. We acted with camaraderie while thinking, no thanks, all the same.

In 1965 when I turned seventeen I started having driving lessons, first with Dad, later with Mum. I don't remember how long it took for us to give up in either case, but it wasn't long. At that time you could apply for a provisional motorcycle licence at sixteen and a provisional car licence at seventeen. As soon as I gave up on the driving lessons, and driving school lessons were out of my financial range, I started looking for a bike. I was dead set on something big. With a provisional licence a learner could ride anything up to and including a 250cc bike, but with a sidecar fitted – or 'chair' as they were known – you could go up to any size of engine. So guys either bought a moped, or a 175cc BSA Bantam, an Ariel Arrow (a 2-stroke very popular with learners then), or if they could afford it, went straight to a pretty BSA 250cc C15. There was also the Triumph Tiger Cub, which held strong appeal. These 250cc models looked very tasty, even wearing L plates. The alternative approach would be to buy a combination. This could be any size as long as the sidecar was attached.

When the rider passed his driving test he could change his 175cc or 250cc for a bigger machine. Or likewise, the owner of a combo with a bigger engine could detach the 'chair' and go solo. The ultimate aim would be for a Triumph Bonneville 650cc twin, a Beezer Golden Rocket (a Goldie) 650cc, or a Norton Dominator 750cc; some of the big machines then dominating the motorcycling scene. The uncoupling of a sidecar could be as disconcerting as upgrading from a small bike to a big twin, if not more so. The handling was entirely different.

For the provisional driving licence, and the 250cc-limit learner law, we have to thank Ernest Marples, minister of transport in Harold Macmillan's 1959 cabinet. He was also responsible for bringing in parking meters, wardens and yellow lines, not to mention the Road Traffic Act, legislation introduced to address the growing problems of congestion and road accidents. The year 1959 also saw Britain's first motorway, the M1, open. The MOT test became compulsory for vehicles aged ten years or above. Eventually the road safety laws lead to the breathalyser, too. In 1962 Marples introduced the Transport Act that would give birth to the 'Beeching report', and the closing of one third of Britain's passenger railways and stations, a move that would seem decidedly to exacerbate the road problems. At the time Marples was lampooned endlessly by newspaper cartoonists as his own mode of transport was a push bike. More ominous was the fact that old Ernest was the creator of Marples Ridgeway, a civil engineering firm that would flourish throughout post-war regeneration. A growing public distrust forced the minister to transfer his shareholding in his road-building company to his wife. Marples Ridgeway was contracted to build Hammersmith and Chiswick flyovers, and a southern extension to the M1. Then, in 1964, Ernie and the rest of the Tory government were thrown out with the bathwater in the shake-up that had started with Christine Keeler and ended with Harold Wilson. But for all of the above, Ernie quite possibly has a lot to answer for. In 1975, Baron Marples of Wallasey became a tax exile in Monaco.

There was another breed of biker, who started with a big machine with a 'chair' in order to ride a more powerful bike, and never bothered with the test, the L plates gradually bleaching to white in the summer and ultimately getting left in the family garage, or in my case, parked in the street outside.

A whole culture evolved around combos and the desire to acquire a decent-looking chair, a 'bullet' being ideal, looking as smart hitched to a big machine as a solo ride of the same variety. The trouble was, most combos were bought second hand from family men, and sported hefty and ugly double-adult sidecars, coach-built affairs the size of a garden shed. We would heave the top off these, leaving them looking like a rowing boat that happened to have a little door in its side, better but not really cool. Some guys took the body off the frame completely, leaving what amounted to a vehicle that was extremely dodgy to handle. Sometimes a soapbox, or even literally an armchair, would be bolted to the frame, lending another dimension to the name 'chair'.

One guy in New Addington had a tuned and beautiful Vincent Black Shadow with a bare frame. It must have been like handling one of the fastest and most powerful bikes in the world with a third wheel on one side. He never seemed to have L plates, and I believe he had a full licence. He just liked his Vincent with a side frame – he'd got used to it. He would be seen haring around the estate, garnering a lot of respect both for the black beast he rode, and for his riding skills.

Pete Bruce, Chris and I belonged to a group who believed in embellishing our combos with enough bling to take them into another category of bike. We replaced the standard handlebars with ape-hangers, mounted small teardrop-shaped fuel tanks (as we'd seen the Yanks doing with their choppers), tried to find a bucket seat to replace the cumbersome and conformist two-seater plastic saddle, and made the chair as decorative as possible. By the time we'd finished with them, our rides would look like cowboy machines, statements. The machines went with our clothes – still the ice-blue jeans, leathers and caps, with the obligatory touch of *de rigueur* cheap wraparound shades. The look of our combos, together with our sartorial leanings, said that we were Rockers, not ton-up boys, café racers or motorcycle enthusiasts.

Of course, we were laughed at or hated. We were the kiddies who hung out 'inside' the café, eating egg and chips, drinking coffee, feeding the jukebox, comparing cap and jacket decoration, combing our hair, posing. Real bikers, the ton-up boys, the Lewis Leather boys, hung around outside: talking bikes, studying bikes, laughing, smoking. It was serious business, this business of bikes. They drank their tea outside, ate their sausage sandwiches outside. The advice we got from these road kings was not to put studs in a leather jacket as that stopped them from being waterproof. SO WHAT? We were all about the style surrounding the bikes. We were the 'Mods and Rockers' generation.

The one and only problem these café kings had with Mods was their mode of transport: their scooters. They were the only item of comparison they could grasp. We had nothing much against Mods at all. It was all a lovely ridiculous excuse to rampage and freak out the staid English squares in our way. We knew what the Mods were doing, we had grown up together on the estates, and they were hip to us too. The only object of derision was a mid.

Actually there was no such thing as a mid, we made them up. We wanted to make the statement that both sides of this newspaper-created fence were invented by 'us' and the purpose of them both was to shake up the straight citizens. Shake up Mr. Jones at Margate. Kathy's Irish father, while watching a TV news item about the seaside scuffles, expressed the view that this was the predominant thing about all the fuss. All at once I could see a new angle on it all. It wasn't about one lot hating another lot. It was about both lots seriously getting up the noses of the deckchair lot, the pre-war self-satisfied lot. Sedition against sedation. I also came to understand something about what being Irish was about.

At dance halls Mods asked us where we got our hats. We ignored them as it felt unseemly to discuss clothes as a prelude to a fight. Our mob would go in a van to Wimbledon Palais. We would get ourselves into a circle and do Ringo's Dog, mock-punching each other. Then slowly turn it into punching other dancers. Eventually an ugly gang of the bigger, harder Mod blokes would be surrounding us, unsurprisingly, and we would edge away to the side of the dance floor before the song was over, as nothing could happen until then. At a side door Pete would say to a uniformed old guard, 'Let us out.'

To which the old guard would say, 'No exit through here, lads.'

'Let us out or there's gonna be a blood bath. *Ours*,' Pete would reply. The panic-stricken guard would open the door. On the other side of the door we would laugh at our silly prank till it hurt, and on the inside the hard blokes would be laughing too. It was *ballet*.

So back at the café, the ton-up boys were not part of our secret world. They had their waterproofs, skid lids (crash helmets), racing saddles, clip-ons. Marvellous machines, in top running order. Legal speed. And we couldn't care less.

Our little group had a hang-up with all things Yank. I loved Harleys. And what was an Indian? There was a guy called Harley Pete. He had a red Electra-glide, with the original police siren still fitted. One night Chris and I were strolling home, pre-bikes, along Saltbox Hill. We heard Pete's siren behind us, jumped back; he skimmed the bank on his way past on that full-dress machine with a wide grin on his face. Yes! I wanted something big. At the time there was only a handful of 1000cc machines being made. The Vincent Black Shadow was one (and was held in the utmost respect by all bikers).

Harleys came with 1250cc motors, which was awesome, but they were sneered at by the UK bike set, mostly. Too slow, too heavy, too gaudy. We'd heard there was a 750cc model. Even guys in our gang would say, 'You don't want to buy a Harley. They drink petrol, you can't get the parts. You can't drop a Harley. If you do, you'll never get up.' I was headstrong about a 1000cc machine. The figure itself was like magic to me. And suddenly there was a 1948 Ariel Square Four for sale.

It had the aforementioned double adult sidecar, the top of which I tore off straight away. Later I bought some ape-hanger handlebars, which I never fitted because I never got round to lengthening the throttle, clutch and front brake cables, in order to facilitate the higher bars. I acquired a new teardrop tank to replace the original enormous Ariel tank. Took the old one off, and never got round to fitting the new one. I did try to spray paint the new tank. I can't spray paint.

Before all these changes failed to happen, somewhere around spring '65, I took the combo out for its first run. Chris was in the sidecar, with another kid called Norman, who sat in front. Norman had been in our class and had spent a lot of his school years as an object of ridicule. He was overweight, with bottle-bottom-thick glasses and spent all his time in class sneaking his hands under his desk top and retrieving crisps he'd bought at the tuck shop. He had rotten teeth too. When people picked on him, he used to spit out 'You P'astard!' It came as a surprise after we all left school that he got himself a Honda 125 and was seen riding around the estate. Next, he passed his test and moved up to a BSA 250cc. And he was a good rider. We had really taken up hanging with him after Chris and I started our Rocker lark. When Norman still had the Honda, he and Chris were riding through Streatham with a number of other bikers when Norman pulled up alongside a Mod's scooter and started undoing bits on the pannier. The scooter boy rode off pretty quickly when the lights changed. It was so unlike Norman on the surface, but he was full of surprises.

Some time before, as Chris and I were strolling along the lane on the way home one day, we came up to a car that had stopped on the crest of a hill at the end of a blind bend. There was a couple in the car, and the guy started asking us the way to somewhere. Suddenly round the blind bend a 250cc appeared, in the wrong lane, the lane we were standing in. The boy in charge of the 250 was a near neighbour of Chris's called Dave Staplehurst, and Norman was on the back. Staplehurst had chosen to aim for us to avoid the car! He yelled 'Get outta the way!' and we jumped up on the steep-sloping bank. Chris was in front and caught the handlebars in the stomach, which caused him some pain for a while. The other three of us were unscathed. The couple in the car drove off with their mouths open.

On my first outing with the Ariel Square Four, with Chris and Norman in the sidecar, I pulled out onto King Henry's Drive, straight along to Vulcan Way, the factory estate where I had my first job at Warner Glass, and turned right onto the estate. It was a weekend: the factories were closed, it was quiet, with parked cars but not a soul about. I took the turn too fast and lost control. Somehow we veered to the left and mounted the footpath. For some unexplainable reason I accelerated along the footpath, not hearing Norman's anguished pleas of 'Brake, brake! You P'astard!' My steering was good enough to negotiate the path without hitting any lamp posts or the wall to our left. Eventually we came to a stop. I must have finally heard Norman. At the end of this exhilarating run, a few spokes were broken on the sidecar wheel, and the petrol cap had flown off, spilling quite a lot of petrol over Norman and Chris. Norman's glasses were quite ruined. I rode the beast back to my house, and then Norman noticed that a couple of HT leads had melted their insulation covering against the engine block. How and when did this happen, pondered Norman. 'Hey, the engine is red hot. Brian, did you change up from first gear?' Well, no, I was a bit stunned on the way home, to be frank. So from that day on my Ariel Square Four 1000cc combo had broken spokes in its sidecar wheel and live HT leads threatening to earth against the engine block. I tried not to spill any more petrol, in case there was a spark.

Some time later Norman took Chris and me out on the Ariel. I'd been having some trouble with the steering. For instance, gassing up at the Addington Village garage, I rode the combo straight into the low brick wall by the exit – I demolished it and rode away before anyone saw me. Later Norman took the combo out to see if he could suss out the problem, as he was the most experienced motorcyclist out of all of us. The bike started to do this whipping thing with the bars, and even Norman couldn't stop it. The three of us rode the combo into a ditch out beside a lonely Kent field.

I did eventually learn to handle my 'Squariel'. I used to ride it to work when I was working as a mechanic over at Selhurst later in '65. One thing I was chicken about was the crest at the top of Saltbox Hill. It needed skilled clutch control, and the Saltbox Café was immediately around to the right as soon as you let the clutch in. So you had to sit at the main Westerham Road until it was clear, then let in the clutch on this sheer incline and immediately swing to your right into the parking area round the café. What I did instead was ride out through Addington to West Wickham through to the Westerham Road and approach the Saltbox from the main road, turning into it across the road. Check it out on a road map; it's miles out of the way. One day I left the machine to get an MOT test at a garage in Addiscombe on the way to the job. When I returned after work to collect my bike, the boss at the garage told me to take it away as soon as possible, or he would call the police. So, no test pass, then? He objected to the broken spokes and the live leads, and a number of other things. This was the beginning of the end for that combo.

There was an adage that said, a silly Rocker is a dead Rocker. This pertained to road safety, mainly. Well, I never did do the ton. I never owned a bike that could.

Meeting on a Bus

When all those hordes of Mods descended upon Margate and Brighton in 1964, the original Modernists looked on and decreed, 'That's the end of it then.' It would be four years later that a few of us 'freaks' would be gathered in one flat or another and stonedly joking back and forth, 'We had your lot in Margate!' Yes, we were all together still, and I believe always had been. Boom babies.

A story that Alan Male, an ex-Mod who would later become my best friend for a while, told me says a great deal about the south London Mod scene, and is also very funny. A large group of Mods from Croydon, among them the group known as the Saxone Boys, had upset the Mods from Streatham, known usually as the Streatham lot. Apparently the Streatham lot massed on their home patch, and when there was a large enough group of them, literally hundreds, they moved up the London Road, which runs from Streatham through Norbury and Thornton Heath to Croydon (on its way from Westminster Bridge all the way to Brighton). Their destination was for a pre-arranged bundle with the Croydon boys, who had set off in the opposite direction, also in their hundreds, in order that the two gangs should meet halfway. The problem was that they missed each other! No-one could ever figure out how they did it, but both sides got a huge laugh out of it, which probably went towards healing any rift.

On most of our trips to Charing Cross to get studs from Badges and Equipment, Chris and I would wander into Soho. I still clearly remember having coffees at the counter of the 2is in

Old Compton Street, gazing at the pictures on the walls of Marty Wilde, Vince Taylor, Wee Willie Harris, *et al*, and thinking, Jeez, this place is still here! It had been the epicentre of British rock 'n' roll, but was on its last legs by the mid-sixties. We would hang around there, over one cup of frothy coffee, I don't think grasping the irony of doing what teenagers had always done in such places. The man serving the foaming lukewarm brew was of vaguely Italian or maybe Cypriot stock, and was jolly and sweaty. I think the original ownership had long changed hands. We didn't think to check out the basement where all that skiffle and early rock 'n' roll had happened. But the walls up in the café carried the atmosphere, with red paint that had seen brighter days, and all sorts of guitars and musical shapes painted over pictures of rock 'n' roll stars, giving an overall feel of a time so vibrant yet so recently gone. It did, as a coffee bar, poke its nose into the seventies, just.

At some point late in the summer of 1965 I stopped going to the Saltbox, partly because the Squariel couldn't get an MOT, but mainly because the scene was dulling for me. Chris had got himself a nice old BSA 600, ex-AA, which was a good runner. When I dropped out of the scene I imagined he would carry on for a while, but I found out later he had started riding his combo into other areas and other scenes. There would be periods of time when Chris and I didn't see each other, and what followed was one of them.

Both of us had been getting increasingly perturbed by a creeping fascism that some of our Rocker chums were subscribing to. Chris and I had always been very Bohemian, we even thought of ourselves as 'Beatniks' long before the notion of becoming Rockers entered our heads. In particular, Chris had been greatly interested in the movement for civil liberties in the United States. He had even written to Dr Martin Luther King, at the age of fifteen! The summer we were Rockers, Chris bought a book called *A Matter of Colour* by Lorraine Hansberry, an amazing book containing some horrifying photographs, including one of a lynching in the South from the 1930s, which we were appalled by. My interest in things Southern had been inspired by Elvis and the Blues, and I was already aware of Southern racism. But that book shocked me, and made me realise how politicised my friend was. While we found the growing use of Nazi insignia on sidecars and jackets disturbing, we also started getting more flak for our style and opinions, which was beginning to turn ugly with time.

In the years that followed, the Nightingale would become a centre for both rock 'n' roll revival gigs and the base for an unchartered chapter of Hells Angels, with our old mate Pete Bruce as the prez.

In late 1965, I started attending Croydon Technical College one day a week, paid for by the garage firm I worked at, as part of the City & Guilds apprenticeship deal. Most apprenticed young men didn't mind being grease monkeys all week, and used the day release as an excuse to stay in bed. For me it was the other way round. I preferred the day in college to the job. An hour at the end of the day was spent on Social Studies, and as a plus I got to hang with the art students in the canteen, experiencing the ghosts of a life I had only just missed out on.

Outside of college, life was getting dull. At some point I ran into Chris on a bus going home from my day at college. We hadn't seen each other since the Saltbox days, before my bike failed the MOT and I 'disappeared' from the Rocker scene. Chris's image had changed somewhat and his jean jacket was covered in pin badges with slogans on them where there had once been studs. His hair had grown somewhat. He was talking about something called the Beat scene.

Cadillacs to Cosmopolitans

My musical career had kept up during these first years after school, but without the same level of enthusiasm. Having been conditioned to think that a career in music would not be possible, I let that particular dream take a back seat, and just focused on being young and foolish.

For a time, I tended to be led by the nose by others more musically keen. Back in September 1964, the month I started my first proper job, and just as I was getting seriously into the Rocker thing, Dave the Liar, with whom I had stayed friends since the Classics days, but without 'doing' anything musical with him, asked me to join him in a group with two older guys, singer Ronnie Diamond and bass guitarist Dave Dirtylegs (I never knew the story behind this nickname), who had both been in a local rock combo based in Norbury, called the Partizans. So the other two guys were kind of local legends. We called ourselves Ron Diamond and the Shakin' Sound, which was Dave's idea, and sort of an up-to-date sounding moniker. Come that November we entered ourselves into the 1964 Red Cross Beat Contest – notice how that had changed its name yet again to suit the times (everything that had been rock before the Beatles was now 'beat') since Dave and I had entered the previous year as part of the bogus Syndicate One.

Our material at this time was still basically rhythm and blues, the kind of stuff the Rolling Stones were covering. The irony was that Ronnie and Dirtylegs were more familiar with the Chuck

Berry originals, for instance, and had a preference for them. In the face of the appeal the Stones had with their look as well as their music, Ronnie thought they looked like prats. He took it upon himself to come round to my parents' flat with a few records by the likes of Berry, Jerry Lee Lewis, Fats Domino and Little Richard. Ron was also way ahead of the curve in being a huge Johnny Cash fan, mainly the early Sun material, and had affected a pretty good imitation of his hero's vocals. Ron was a mentor to me, turning me on to the stuff I had missed by being a bit younger.

I owned a tape recorder at the time, upon which Dave and I recorded many bedroom sessions. Reel-to-reel machines were quite an option for some young guys, as well as Dansette record players. I knew more than one guy who had, for instance, the complete Buddy Holly on a tape reel, all from borrowed records. I borrowed Ron's collection of 78s, every one of them on London American, and taped them. Another great record Ron owned was Carl Perkins' *Dance Album*. Before borrowing this wondrous LP I had not had the pleasure of hearing the original 'Blue Suede Shoes', and this and the other tracks were a revelation in their stripped-down production, country hick vocals drenched in echo, great guitar breaks and slapped double bass. On top of that were the swinging feel of the band and the occasionally weird subject matter, as in 'Wrong Yo Yo' and songs about atom bombs in Tennessee. I remember first hearing the Beatles' LP *Beatles For Sale* in December 1964 at the local church youth club. That album contains versions of two of the tracks on Carl's album, and as I already knew the originals by then, the Fabs' versions tended to lower my estimation of the group still further.

The same thing happened with the Stones, who I had favoured as a kind of anti-Moptops, as well as liking their coming on like a genuine blues band. At some point in '64 I bought a compilation LP of blues released on Chess Records. I remember standing in a listening booth in Allders department store in Croydon with Dad, having asked the young Saturday assistant girl to drop the sapphire on Lowell Fulson's 'Reconsider Baby'. I wanted to compare it with Elvis's version on *Elvis Is Back!* and the easy loping shuffle of Fulson's blues under a full twelve bars of stuttering guitar intro sold me on a new sound. Back at home the LP introduced me to Muddy Waters' versions of some things I'd heard the Stones crash through at a hundred miles an hour. While it took me some time to get my head around the sounds of Muddy and Little Walter's amped-up mouth harp, it stopped me short of bothering with a Stones album for many years to come. Didn't change my mind about Elvis though.

The Chess LP also had Howlin' Wolf's great 'Smokestack Lightnin'' on it. This monster of a record was one of a few singles issued belatedly in the UK in the early sixties on the back of the 'R&B boom'. Wolf's record actually went top fifty in June 1964. Another single, and one I bought, John Lee Hooker's 'Dimples', went top thirty the same month. I bought Hooker's record on the same day as 'Rosalyn' by the Pretty Things, who I thought topped the Stones in most departments. What a time to be record shopping, though, and mostly this was down to the radio pirates. Times would rarely be as good after they were taken off the air three years later.

The result of the 1964 Red Cross Beat Contest was the same as the previous year for us. Before Christmas we enlisted a rhythm guitarist named Eddy, whose name is all that remains of him in my memory. Early in the new year, Dave decided to up and leave us, just as he had with the Classics, and once again I stayed on. Someone found a new guitarist named Spider Webb, and Ron, true to his roots, re-named the outfit Johnny Fleetwood and the Cadillacs. Next, Dirtylegs left and was replaced by another ex-Partizan, Alan Mac. The main regular gig we played under the new name was way over in Canning Town in east London, a pub called the Bridge House. This venue would become a well-known rock 'n' roll pub in the seventies, too late for us. But let me state here, we were there first, and as our repertoire had reverted to the fifties thanks to Ron taking control, we rocked.

Johnny Fleetwood and the Cadillacs did not make it as far as the following spring, 1965. After a period of quiet as far as playing drums was concerned, I got a call from Ron asking me to join a group he'd started singing with. They were called the Cosmopolitans, and they had formed in 1959. The Cosmopolitans were a regular guitar, bass and drums group, but tended to book themselves out as a sort of modern dance band. We consequently found ourselves at Young Conservatives dances, hotel do's, weddings and other very square gigs. We even did some work as the pit orchestra for a children's pantomime. It meant that Ronnie and I quickly became the odd ones out, and this pushed us together more as mates. He drove a Mark 1 Ford that he'd bought from Alan Mac, with flames painted up the side. I, still seventeen, the baby of the group, fell under his influence. Ron could be thought of as a kind of 'Fonz' but with lashings more cool. He jived with two partners at once; painted his copy of 'Brand New Cadillac', a number we did in the group, with gold paint, and hung it on his wall. It would not play any more, of course, but he thought so highly of it, he felt it was worth the sacrifice! Ronnie got very friendly with my old man, and in fact, they stayed mates for some years.

The most interesting gig we played as the Cosmopolitans was at a restaurant called the Queen's Grill that sat right next to Queen's Ice Rink on Queensway in Bayswater. We played every Saturday for most of my tenure with the group. There was a Cosmopolitans publicity postcard in the front window of the restaurant. Fame on Queensway! One would walk through a long narrow front part of the restaurant to the back, where the room opened out to a square shape. On the left of the square there was a small stage, with a few more tables set up opposite. We did two sets, with a free supper thrown in during the break, which we were given back in the kitchen. There we would be regaled with stories by Lawny the Irish chef, who was one reason among many that I tended towards the belief in my youthful mind that there were many more gay men north of the river than south.

Dad would often drive me up to Bayswater with my kit. On these occasions he would sit with the patrons in front of the stage. There was one fellow, very well suited with a mid-Atlantic accent, who would talk to Dad all night when he was there. Used to invite him for moonlight swims over at the Serpentine. Of course, Dad never went, he had to take me home! Mum took me to the gig sometimes, but she always disappeared immediately and came back for me at the end of the evening. I never wondered too hard where she was off to. If Ronnie's car was running I would go with him.

Queensway, although it is hard to imagine now, had a certain Bohemian atmosphere back in the mid-sixties. Live music was happening up and down the street in many of the little cafés. There was a Joan Baez-type character who walked among the tables in one place, serenading the clients with protest songs, and at La Palette, diners were given a palette and paints and encouraged to render likenesses of a nude model while they sipped their coffee.

After a year the guys in the band decided to recruit a young female singer called Storine, a very pretty Asian girl. The idea, as it was explained, was to add some variety to the repertoire. One night at the Queen's Grill Ronnie was late getting back for the second set, too busy laughing with Lawny perhaps, and Storine took to the stage and belted out one of Ronnie's rockers – she usually handled the pop stuff. She was good, and Ron and I saw the writing on the wall. Ronnie's notice came quickly after that. In fact, he may even have held back from that second set on purpose. Either way, Storine was now our only singer.

The Cosmopolitans dragged on through 1966, which turned out to be a time of much soul-searching for me. The music I was playing had little, if anything, to do with the stuff I was listening to at home or at gigs. My feelings for the Cosmopolitans were not helped by yet another recruitment in the form of a keyboard player who seemed to add a touch of the modern to a seriously dated outfit. Nothing could cure my waning interest in the ailing Cosmopolitans.

Subterranean Homesick Blues

Alan Young, my friend who had quit school to emigrate to New Zealand, came back in 1966. Alan had always seemed older in his ways than I, and the emigration had added to that, with him leaving school before the legal age, and travelling the world. While he was in New Zealand Alan and I kept in touch by letter. The first letter came from him, and mentioned that he knew about me and Kathy. Whoops. Nice start.

When his family got to Wellington they all got jobs and saved like crazy because they knew immediately that they wanted to come back to Blighty. Part of the £10 emigration deal was that you had to stay two years or you were liable for the passage *both* ways. So they stayed two years and saved enough to get back.

On the journey out they had sailed through the east and on the way back they sailed through the Panama Canal. I guess the ships only went in those set directions. Each journey took about two months, so Alan had really seen something of the world by the time he was eighteen, taking all that travel and work into consideration. When he arrived back in England in May of '66 he came round to see me straight away.

He told me that none of his cousins or any of the guys he'd been hanging out with before he left had bothered to write. I was the only one. So he made a point of coming round and knocking on our door one teatime out of the blue. I guess we had the girlfriend in common too, which might have added something to our bond. From that day on Alan and I hung out most of the time. The first time Alan met up with Kathy after his return, I was with him. Innocent enough, but probably not the right thing to do. What made it all that much stranger was that Kathy, now seventeen, had a baby son. For me, seeing Kathy again, and as a young mother, was very emotional. Must have been the same for Alan, only he and I didn't ever discuss it on an emotional level.

He had saved up a thousand pounds. This was 1966, and believe me, a thou in cash was an awesome amount of money for a young chap to be holding back then. He bought a grey Minivan with some of it, and we started tooling around Croydon and then ventured north of the river. Again, in 1966 one could drive straight up to London, over Chelsea Bridge, go across to Soho, Leicester Square, Grosvenor Square, *anywhere* you needed to go, and just *park*.

Grosvenor Square was the scene of one of our most innocent japes. As Alan had done some travelling, we started talking about the United States. Somehow I thought he was more sussed than I, but *both* of us were so green we strolled into the US Embassy and asked for an interview. We got one all right, and the polite chap behind the desk informed us that there was no way we could obtain visas for working in the United States without this and that . . . and that and this . . . and then we suggested to the polite man that perhaps we could get a flight over, and get jobs when we got there! Or even, and I swear we said this, fly to Canada and enter the States from there! *Whaaat?* Who did we think we were talking to? We got a brief but firm lecture before being shown the way out. I hope we didn't mess things up for a generation who tried this very thing in the years to come and found that the authorities were wise to them!

That little escapade at the US Embassy did more than make me feel small. It put me off even attempting to travel west for many years. When I eventually did, in the late seventies, when visitors' visas were still necessary, I was as nervous as hell going through the motions. Ten years had not allayed my fear. Later still I would spend a lot of time Stateside, but in the meantime I watched as a restless generation took off both west and east over the next few years. I wish I had made it to the States in '66, that's for sure!

Not long after Alan's return to England, he and I visited our old school. We saw Mr. Sutherland, the technical drawing master, a very upright regimental type, who had been a huge but unlikely fan of the Shadows. He liked me, and Tech Drawing was the *only* subject I had excelled in at GCE. He told me he was surprised to see me, as Dave James had informed him that I was in the States playing piano! Obviously, the occasion of this lie was a gig that Dave played at the school, which would have been just prior to our visit. I like to think that Mr Sutherland had inquired after me at the gig, as he may have been expecting me to be playing with Dave on that occasion. But, how prophetic of Dave the Liar. He was a good few years too soon, and had me down on the wrong instrument; the first time I played on American soil would be in 1982, in New York, on tenor sax.

Alan and I did a lot of clubbing in both south London and 'up west'. He had returned from Kiwi-land with a love of rhythm and blues, so our musical tastes had kept abreast. One of the places we used to frequent was Chislehurst Caves in Kent. This was a fantastic underground club snaking over a series of tunnels. It was another place that had opened for business originally as a jazz club.

The Caves had been used as the location for the film *Beat Girl* in 1960, and the scenes in the film where young Beat types are seen jiving or sitting around expounding had not changed beyond some minor fashion details by 1966. The top acts of the time appeared at the club, and there would be DJs too – that is, at the same time. A peculiarity of the Caves was the acoustics. You could stand watching a band at one of the little stages, then wander off down a tunnel and come to a spot where the DJ might be spinning, say, 'When A Man Loves A Woman' – a big hit in both the charts and in the clubs – with a large group of Mods slow dancing to it. And the sound from the two sources would not overlap. Alan and I were going there during the height of the trend for soul bands. We watched a band with a horn section in there one night. Someone in the band had a starting pistol that he would occasionally fire on the backbeat during exuberant solos. The crack from that pistol in the Caves was deafening.

They used to warn punters not to wander off while they were in the Caves, as they might get lost. There were rumours about people who disappeared and were never seen again. The Caves were said to be haunted. Since the seventies the Caves have been hired for private parties. I went to a couple.

Alan and I also went to a place along the London Road called Under the Olive Tree. It was mostly known as the Olive Tree. Some of my ex-Mod mates used to score pills there. It was a coffee bar that hosted folk music, and was very close to the Orchid Ballroom in Purley, our very own Palais de Dance, scene of teenage dances all through the sixties. And of course, before us, our uncles and aunties in the forties and fifties. My aunty used to say she saw Ray Ellington there regularly (he of the *Goon Show*). We saw the Who, Small Faces, Solomon Burke and Cliff Bennett there. It's a fitness centre now.

Up in town we frequented the Flamingo on Georgie Fame nights, and caught Eric Clapton playing with John Mayall at the Marquee, the one on Wardour Street. Oddly, though we caught both these seminal acts late in the day, so to speak, we had literally wandered in and caught them without exposure to any brouhaha first. Suffice to say, we were enough impressed to go back for more. In the case of Georgie, I had been aware of his career since Kathy was a fan back in the days when she was a Mod and I was a Rocker. Now I was trailing in her footsteps.

We had started to go to the Flamingo after Georgie's huge 'Get

Away' hit, and since he had become so popular a club draw, the place was always shoulder-to-shoulder packed, and as hot as a sauna. We knew nothing about the power of television or a hit record in those days. We assumed the Flamingo had always been like this, but looking back, it is obvious that the usual crowd of Mods, dolly birds and West Indians had been greatly expanded by the Fame hit. At this time, it seems, the Georgie Fame and the Blue Flames' residency had been extended, probably set up before the Gunnell brothers, who ran the all-nighter at the club, knew the new record would be such a hit. Georgie left at the end of this run, and split the Blue Flames.

The sweat from that basement club caused me to spend a good deal of my meagre wages on dry cleaning.

Dave's West End Rambles

'I'm not getting in the back, I've been on *Top of the Pops*.'

Thus spoke Johnny Blunt the first time I ever met him. I had turned up at his parents' house in Monks Hill with Dave the Liar and Alan in the Minivan.

I split my sides at John's camp humour, and climbed in the back of the little van.

In March 1966, Johnny, a local lad from Monks Hill estate, had been asked to join the Searchers. At the time the Liverpool lads were on their last go-round chart-wise. They were still a big name, such that any new discs would see them on to *Ready Steady Go!* and *Top of the Pops*, but the records were climbing lower and lower in the hit listings. I had never heard of the Trees, the local group John had been picked from to join the Searchers, but it turned out they were quite a well-known R&B outfit locally, and Dave had been their singer for a spell. The story goes that he had forsaken guitar for the frontman position, destroying microphones in an attempt at aping Roger Daltrey. He was sacked, and it was John who'd had to tell him.

It was just after John had upgraded to the Searchers that Dave had Alan take us in his new grey Minivan over to John's parents' house. Dave was always coming round and taking me somewhere, I believed as a companion. On this occasion Dave was looking to rejoin the Trees now that John had left.

John's day job had been with Chapman & Sons, builders and coal merchants at West Croydon. One day, when John was still a coal-deliverer's mate, he had pulled into a local hospital to deliver coal. Suddenly a figure leapt onto the running board of the lorry – none other than Dave the Liar, who showed John his bandaged wrists. He was a guest of the hospital after having tried to end it all, his mental problems already having been diagnosed at seventeen years old. Dave must have had problems beyond anything we knew.

A typical Dave adventure from around this time found me sitting in the Soho offices of Arthur Howes. Now, at this time, Howes was one of the absolutely top agents in the country. Dave arrived at my house one afternoon and persuaded me to come up west to see the agent. I thought I was in for some embarrassment, but kept it to myself and went along for the gas.

So there we were in the reception area of this 'swanky' West End office, which was in fact in Greek Street, at an address that would later house Private Eye, in the heart of what was then the music business in London – parallel to Wardour Street, a stone's throw from Great Windmill Street, and near enough to any one of a dozen salt beef bars. Think the film *Expresso Bongo* and you're there. The receptionist told Dave and me to sit down, with a familiar 'Oh, hello, Dave.' Already I was thinking, What?

Dave was too wired to sit still and spent the next few minutes chatting to the receptionist. Okay, experience has told me that the office, like a hundred others at that time, was fake wood-panelled and cheap, but I was young and impressionable. Very well-known people seemed to be entering and exiting offices, but this might be my memory playing tricks. Suddenly Mr. Howes stepped out of his own office and said, 'Hello, Dave.' I was gobsmacked. I think what followed was a conversation about how Arthur was a little busy at the moment, or it is possible that Dave was ushered into the inner sanctum for a short while. Not me, no-one introduced me.

The picture was this. Dave was such a bullshitter that he had bullshitted his way into as big an agency as you could get, and the man who owned the agency gave him his time, *with no appointment.*

Around this time Dave changed his surname from James to Antony, leading to some confusion for future annotators. There was a group called Dave Antony's Moods, but that was a different Dave Antony, although *our* Dave definitely used that group name at some point. He also stole the name 'the Buzz' from David Jones of Beckenham, who was soon to alter his own second name to Bowie.

With a guitarist called Keith Aldridge, Dave had previously been in the League of Gentlemen, a group created mainly for backing R&B artists from the States. This group should not be confused with the later one that included Robert Fripp.

Dave, with Keith, joined a group from Liverpool called the Anzacs, with the express purpose of playing gigs in Germany. They also went out as a rogue version of the Riot Squad, much to the displeasure of the real Riot Squad, which at one time had included drummer Mitch Mitchell. Sound familiar?

Around the same time as Johnny joined the Searchers, Dave played the aforementioned gig at our old school, Fairchildes. This had to be nearly two years after Dave had left school, so how this gig came about I've no idea. Nor which group he was fronting at the time. It seems, though, that Johnny Blunt went along to support his friend. On the rare occasion of a rock gig at school, pupils from the girls' school were invited. John had just joined the Searchers with quite a lot of local publicity, and was duly chased down the school corridors by enthusiastic schoolgirls. Finding where Dave's allocated 'dressing room' was, he hid himself in there for the duration of the gig. When Dave found him there after the show he was furious – John had more or less emptied the hall!

1966 and All That

After fifteen years working with Waterlow & Sons, the *Radio Times* printers, Dad quit and found another job. Waterlows had been taken over and Dad didn't want to move with the new firm out of town to work. So the takeover made him do what my mother had been trying to get him to do for years – find another job. Dad became an accountant for the Rank Organisation in 1963, and sometimes worked Saturday mornings. On Saturday 30 July 1966 he and some colleagues stayed on at the office to watch the match. You know, *the Match*. One of those colleagues was probably his young friend, Angelique, the one I knew about but my mother did not. Mum had left us some time around June; Dad said she was in Germany. I was never told the truth about this time by either of them.

My parents had always fought like cat and dog, their rows usually ending with them screaming insults at each other. When I look back over the years with the benefit of hindsight, I realise that *either* he kicked her out because of her ongoing affair with Fred, or she left because of *his* shenanigans with other women, shenanigans that were largely part of her imagination. Why on earth I needed to be spoon-fed a lot of manure from Dad I don't know. And why she could not have spoken to me about it, I also could never see. Especially since in later years I still didn't get to the truth!

Back in 1962 Mum had met Fred, who, with a job as an architectural designer, was both earning a high salary and travelling abroad, and they were going to shows, dinners, the opera, generally seeing much of each other. That was when she started to be out in the evening sometimes. She was doing the things she wanted to do, meeting the people she wanted to meet. Her reason for flying off 'to Germany' was most likely to put a punctuation mark in her life. Whatever the reason at the time, it seems it was 'indefinite'. When I look back on all this now, I believe Dad probably kicked her out. And then lied to me.

I was about to embark on an adventure in Germany myself. In June 1966 Dave formed a group with me and Tony Perry, to play gigs in Germany. We even had some rehearsals round at my flat. The other two guys tried to convince me that my image needed some upgrading, as I was still decidedly Rocker in my apparel. Mum was already gone by now, and Dad insisted on writing a letter asking her if it was okay for me to go with Dave and Tony to Germany. I thought it was weak of my father, still giving her the last say in my life decisions, especially as she wasn't even around. Why he did not instruct me to write the letter, I did not think to question. Mum replied to Dad's letter, saying I must do what I wanted to do, and that I should go. I found that very lenient and carefree for her, at the time.

Dave had done the German thing quite a bit throughout the previous year or so, playing with some soul bands and backing up Jack Hammer. But our German trip didn't come about in the end because, according to Dave, Tony had spent too much time worrying Dave about how he was going to get his socks washed. As a sidebar, I must add that there was often a pungent smell of feet round at Dave's house. In fact, it was something occasionally alluded to by other musicians who knew him. Across these many years, I am left wondering if Tony made mention of this and blew our chance of a European fiasco in the making. I never followed in the footsteps of all those groups who played Germany.

On the day of the World Cup final the number one pop single

94

was 'Out of Time' by Chris Farlowe. It was replaced later that month by 'Sunny Afternoon' by the Kinks, which was replaced in turn by Georgie Fame and the Blue Flames' 'Get Away'. 'Get Away' entered the chart on 23 June and, as I mentioned, Alan and I started seeing the Blue Flames at the Flamingo after the record's entry. We were late going to the 'Mingo, but not too late.

The World Cup final was played before a packed Wembley Stadium. At the moment of triumph, the winning goal, at the end of extra time, I was wandering along King Henry's Drive alone, making my way across the estate to Dave's house to tell him about Mum's response to Dad's letter. Someone burst out of their front door shouting, 'We've won! We've won!' At first I had no idea what he was shouting about. When I realised, and understood why the streets were so empty, I felt extremely disconnected. Something that had everything to do with almost everybody had nothing to do with me. My interest in football was so minimal it didn't exist, and had been that way forever, even before the hated cold and muddy torture called games at school.

Many years later, after my mother married Fred, I found out that during the actual World Cup match she was flying with him to Austria, where he had business. Apparently they announced the score over the loudspeakers on the plane. So she had been living in England all along. No wonder Dad wanted to write that letter himself about my trip to Germany.

People in England still speak about the 1966 World Cup final as if it were an historical event on a par with 1066. Perhaps it is. It was certainly an interesting time for me.

On Sunday 31 July, the day after the World Cup final, Alan and I drove up to Berkshire, and the Royal Windsor Racecourse, for the last day of the 6th Windsor Jazz & Blues Festival, headlined by Cream. He and I had become Clapton fans after seeing him at the Marquee with John Mayall, and we later drove around to see more Cream gigs in his grey Minivan. It had only been in a recent

95

issue of *Melody Maker* that Cream's formation was announced, and even then it was a rumour.

At Windsor, Alan and I were wearing new short suede jackets. Mine was grey, his tan, and the jackets incited a gang of little pseudo moddy boys to try to take them off us. (It was a thing little suburban moddies did.) We stared them down, which was easy and amusing. We spent the afternoon and evening digging Georgie Fame (not as exciting to see as he had been at the hyper-sweaty Flamingo) and the Alan Bown Set with Jess Roden on vocals, who impressed us a lot. There were others who have melted away along with some brain cells, but mainly because our patience grew thin waiting for the Cream. When they came on it was drizzling rain. Eric wore a gold lamé jacket and asked if they were loud enough. To which some wag yelled, 'No, *you* louder.' In those days outdoor PA systems still could not cut the mustard. Cream were pretty good, though – this was before the power trio became so contrived.

On the occasions of our going clubbing or to gigs Alan would come and collect me. During this time of enforced bachelorhood for Dad, he would sometimes have Angelique over to visit. I remember coming in one night with Alan, on our way to somewhere else, and we were both impressed with Angelique. I had heard about her, including during a row between Mum and Dad, but had not met her, had never thought I would. She was Beat-looking, brunette and opinionated, and above all, seemingly hip. She asked us all the right questions about where we were going and what we were listening to. But, of course, she was just about our age, and since she was spending her weekend with an older man, probably more mature!

The whole thing about that time Mum was away, which was about three months, was that Dad and I both seemed to be 'off the hook'.

Dad's form of freedom was more abstract. I can't name it,

but he seemed to be doing things he enjoyed while I was out doing whatever I wanted to. He may have been going through a tough time, but we didn't speak about it. At some point a letter apparently came from Mum. Dad said she was asking if she was wanted back. I remember that Dad and I sat down in conference. Again, it was up to me. Apparently I said it would be better with Mum here. I cannot connect with why I would have put it that way. Was I thinking of him? Did I want to be kind, and let her off the hook? Maybe I thought she was in exile and it was not of her own making? I think I was too young to make any decision of that kind. Of course, now I think he probably wanted her back because of me. I never knew.

In 1967, the year following Mum's return home, I would make my first botched attempt at leaving. Dad's mood became unbearable after she came back, our dual bachelorhood now curtailed. If Mum came back for my benefit, it would explain why Dad was so dismissive about everything I did from then on. He had accepted her return for my sake, meaning they were together because of me, an arrangement lasting only another two years, by which time I had successfully left. He had an agenda, and I was now standing in his way. A lot like the way I had been accidentally conceived.

A New Dance Sensation . . .
Sweeping the Studio

Dotted all over London were what I called 'egg box studios', which I so named after the common method of sound-proofing them. It's hard to imagine, in this world where very advanced recordings are made in a bedroom using a computer and digital recording software. It wasn't always that way. Up until the end of the sixties the recording process was a mystery, even for young people playing in groups. And studio owners kept it that way – they were onto a good thing.

You would see what we called 'demo discs' (acetates) lying across someone's kitchen table, like round at Dave's neighbour Ray Neale's house, when he and his brother were in local group the Kingpins. Or a kid might carry one into school to show off that the ragged little bunch of amateurs that he'd done a summer season with at Butlin's had cut a 'disc'. One such kid had been Dave. Dave was responsible for my first taste of recording, which brings us back to a day in September 1966.

Dave was always talking his way into one scam or another. He had got a couple of recording jobs, both to take place on the same day. The first was in the morning and it was at somewhere called Jensen's Studios. Like at so many downscale 'studios' then, we found ourselves on a floor above a small shop, this one in Redhill, Surrey. I was set up with a pair of bongos in a room, and the engineer (who I think was the owner . . . perhaps Jensen himself?) laid a seemingly endless length of cardboard tube, looking like a very large version of what goes through a toilet roll, from the bongos and out of the room. I never saw where the tube went and never saw any other room. I also never knew what I was playing to, I was just instructed through a playback speaker to play a rhythm on the bongos and the engineer apparently recorded a few minutes of it. I was told that the bongo recording was to be used for a poetry LP. I never found that LP, but then I haven't spent much time looking through poetry albums, either.

That afternoon Dave and I, together with Tony, got ourselves to a studio in Bromley, Kent. This time we were hired as session musicians. An Indian chap whose name is lost in the mists of time had created a dance step, and Dave had been commissioned to write a melody for this chap's lyrics and to provide the backing to get it on to tape. The 'song' was called 'The Jig Jog Dance' (ahem, yeah, I know), and the inventor of the dance had the steps all drawn out on a scruffy piece of paper. Now, this studio was a bit more like a regular demo studio, but with no egg boxes as far as I recall. There were three rooms. The drums were set up in one, Dave and Tony (and probably the Jig Jog creator, who sang the song in a strong Indian accent to the tune Dave had written for him) in another. The third room was the control room. Two blokes worked the recording equipment, which my greater experience now tells me was probably a Revox 2-track and a crude mixer, plus a possible Watkins Copycat echo or Binson reverb unit and maybe a home-made limiter. We never set foot in the control room (just as we didn't in later sessions to come), and to me that was part of retaining the 'mystery'. If those people who had set up these various recording firms had let anyone know how simple it was, they'd have been out of business. Which they soon were.

Anyway, the drums had towels laid across them, making them sound like a distant set of cardboard boxes. The rest of the band didn't sound too bad. When I realised I wasn't being offered a demo disc of the song, I later wrote to the studio asking for a recording. What I got back was a short length of tape on a little three-inch reel. I had the tape pressed onto acetate somewhere, and it sounded dreadful.

That was my first day in recording studios. Auspicious beginnings.

Croydon Crawdaddy

Time out for a brief description of an important venue that sat on the northern fringe of our landscape back then. The Star Hotel on London Road at Broad Green hosted the Croydon Jazz Club, part of the club scene that mushroomed in the back rooms of pubs from the early fifties and even rode out the rise of R&B in the early sixties. When the Mersey sound pushed the trad records out of the charts in '63, the post-Stones R&B scene (started by Alexis Korner out of the trad/skiffle scene) took over the jazz clubs. The Star hosted the Croydon Crawdaddy when Georgio Gomelsky opened it in 1963 as a sister venue to his Richmond Crawdaddy. In April 1964 the Croydon Crawdaddy became the Star Club. Crawdaddy bands like the Yardbirds regularly played the Star Hotel. Many a Croydon regular would remember Julie Driscoll taking tickets and stamping hands on the door at the Star. She was the Yardbirds fan club secretary at the time, but was discovered as a singing sensation while working the door. Chris and I had visited the Croydon Crawdaddy as Rockers, and acted surly when the clothes-obsessed Mods asked quite genuinely where we got our gear.

In late '65, when Chris and I briefly parted ways after the Rocker times, he had become a regular at the Croydon Folk Club, held in a small ante-room beside the club room at the back of the Star. A room where my 'functions' band, the Cosmopolitans, would sometimes rehearse. It was here I would eventually see Davy Graham, Gerry Lochran, the Young Tradition, Al Stewart, Bert

Jansch, and our own local heroes, some of whom would become friends, like Jo Ann Kelly, Dave Eggert and a very talented Pete Lieberman.

We saw the precociously gifted and mysterious Jackson C. Frank at the Bridge Folk Club, which took place in an upper room of a pub called the Bridge Hotel in Thornton Heath. Then there was Les Cousins up in the West End where we would go every other Saturday night for an all-nighter run by Alexis Korner, and see Roy Harper regularly, lots more of Al Stewart, some of Peter, Paul & Mary and Alexis Korner himself. When Alexis formed Free At Last with Hughie Flint and Binkie MacKenzie, he gigged at the Star. This was later, in '67, the era in which we saw Jimi Hendrix, Cream, John Mayall, Captain Beefheart, Champion Jack Dupree and many other blues and rock legends at this venue.

Jack Dupree was a volatile character. He appeared at the Star one night in 1967 and before he went on we spotted him in the saloon bar. He was the first man I ever saw wearing earrings. The story went that before he was a musician he was a champion boxer back in New Orleans, and I don't believe Champion Jack ever stopped boxing. Someone in the bar had upset Jack, and he was inviting the guy outside. Someone else was trying to calm Jack down so he could go on and do his set, which we were surprised to learn was made up mainly of risqué humour rather than the barrelhouse boogie we had come to hear. The opening band that night was the Savoy Brown Blues Band, from south London, who included in their ranks a future friend of mine, Martin Stone.

I met Champion Jack again many years later at the 100 Club, and asked him to sign an LP I'd brought with me. He was still the same ornery, rude and ignorant old curmudgeon. He asked me to buy him a drink before he would sign my LP. I asked him what he'd like, and he said, 'White wine.' I turned to the bar to order, but he said, 'Don't get it now. Bring me it when I'm on stage.' So I waited until he was on, and sent my date for the evening up with the wine. I should have just forgotten about it, maybe. The old fool.

Walkin' the Boogie

In summer '66, Alan and I were getting bored with tooling around in his Minivan, doing everything as two blokes on their own. We were having a lot of trouble meeting new people, and that meant girls, and we had outgrown the same old faces on the estate. I remembered that I had run into Chris a couple of months before Alan's return to England, that Chris's new 'scene' had sounded promising and had whetted my appetite. We got in touch.

It transpired that after I had stopped hanging out at the Saltbox, Chris had in fact done the same. However, his BSA was a well-looked-after, nicely running machine, and he had continued to ride around on it, chancing upon a little scene happening on Saturdays at the Gates of Whitgift. These were the gates of the old public school, John Whitgift Trinity, right slap in the centre of Croydon. Trinity was one huge school, too big and standing on too much valuable real estate to last beyond the late sixties. First it was razed to build a two-tiered shopping mall called the Whitgift Centre. This was later replaced by the horror of an even bigger, beroofed shopping experience still called the Whitgift Centre. Back before it was built the Saturday crowd also got together at the Lyons Corner House on the other side of the High Street. This was the CND crowd.

Alan wasn't about to be 'hanging around' at the Whitgift gates, but he was willing to see what action was taking place over the weekend with these 'new' people. The Minivan was that rarity – wheels! We had been ferrying people around quite a bit already, and when we hooked up with Chris he took us, in Alan's wheels, to some rather interesting parties.

I found myself at the Whitgift School Gates on Saturday afternoons. Young Beat types would hand out CND and similar leaflets and generally hang out killing time. Some people just seemed to use the meeting point as exactly that – a wonderfully easy way to chat up interesting people of the opposite sex.

There were also covert meetings of the Young Communists League at a paint factory belonging to the uncle of one of the guys who hung out with that crowd, who was of European Jewish extraction. Chris and I would walk to and from this covert address in an area between West Croydon and Thornton Heath, talking of everything and anything other than communism! For instance there were two small streets we passed along our way, one named Lansdowne Road and one named Neville Road. I would complain that they had my name spelled wrong, and he would chuckle that at least they got the important name right.

Mostly there were parties at the weekends – we became 'Weekend Ravers' – which hosted a plethora of nice upper-middle-class girls who fell for our 'alternative' outlook on life, and who I was beginning to understand were a good reason for getting into the Beat scene; which was also fuelled by cheap wine and cider, and even cheaper little blocks of hash, usually purchased from some local West Indians who saw us coming.

When Alan took up with a regular girlfriend, a girl he had met on the 'scene', I started to hang with Chris a lot more, and it was back to Shanks's and the bus for me.

* * *

The Second World War had brought about a resurgence of an underground club scene that had thrived in the 1920s, in the years after the Great War, and some of the main ingredients remained the same: 'foreign' men, good-time girls, jazz and drugs. This time black sailors and GIs replaced the much-maligned Chinamen from Limehouse as the mythical providers of illicit substances, and were soon replaced themselves by West Indian immigrants. The music was a new generation of jazz and blues, and the drugs were cannabis and speed (initially Benzadrine), replacing the opium and cocaine (the latter to later make a drastic return) in the pages of the yellow press.

As the fifties progressed, the clubs were frequented more and more by young white men and women who learned to love the bop jazz first, and the R&B later. They were followed by disaffected baby boomers needing to escape the humdrum world of office hours, and young women dressed in black, carrying a novel and a lipstick, and, most importantly, an independent attitude, not always having to be in a relationship.

As the earliest be-bop jazz clubs and some West End dance halls were busted for dope, the tabloids ran with the idea of young women keeping company with black men, and sharing their reefers. This was an old trick of the tabloids, harking back to the twenties, with only the drugs, the music and the gentlemen's country of origin having changed. But as the years moved into the later fifties and into the sixties, the 'concern' became a whole generation of youths, both boys and girls, as the music clubs became the places to go.

And in the way that the new black man had replaced the yellow peril of the past, so the yellow peril was replaced by the red menace. As early as 1951 newspapers were warning of communist sympathy among young teenage schoolgirls! Just as how in the Roaring Twenties the Germans had been blamed for the opium traffic, so in the Rockin' Fifties it was maintained that cannabis was a Russian plot.

So the themes of concern over multi-racial mixing, drug taking and general moral abandon were old, but the teenager was the new feckless victim, according to the establishment and its lackey, the press.

And here we were, in 1966, attending covert meetings of the Young Communist League. As for the YCL, it included warring factions in the same way that various Trotsky socialist groups did, and do. Some of the young people I met belonged to other chapters of the YCL, and got involved in jaunts to minor and rarely heard-about communist states in Europe, like parts of Yugoslavia, and other places whose names would have changed today. The groups of travellers were enabled to do this by at least some of them being members of the YCL. Accommodation was the last consideration, however, if the stories I heard about sleeping rough by the sea are anything to go by. These trips amounted to weekend raves like those here but just carried abroad, and I missed them. Another chance to travel missed, at least for the time being. Looking back, many of the travellers were students, so had long vacations in which to travel. With the rest of us, we either had a job we needed to hold down, or we didn't have parents that could pay for our every whim. These guys and girls were very young, with wealthy parents and no experience of life, for all their bluster and pretence.

Mick

Chris introduced me to a motley bunch of interesting people, and one in particular: a certain Mick Gibbs.

Mick had attended Ruskin Grammar, and had only just left in 1965. Mick's poetry had been gathering some note at school, especially a pastiche of Henry V's speech before Harfleur, which drew inspiration from the Mod/Rocker bank holiday battles at Margate and Brighton. Mick was the first to wear a Dada badge at school, and probably was already wearing his hair only just short of a mandatory expulsion.

A group of us, but often just Chris, Mick and I, would board the Circle Line to kill time, waiting for a late scene, usually Cousins. We'd board at, say, Charing Cross, and travel all the way round, back to the same station. Along the way we'd play harmonicas and laugh and talk bullshit. We couldn't afford to sit in the Marquis of Granby or the Black Horse, pubs then frequented by Beats and folky types. Number 49 Greek Street in Soho was a restaurant, and the owners let the basement out first for the Skiffle Cellar and then Les Cousins Folk Cellar (later just Les Cousins Folk Club). My first memories of Greek Street were of a long featureless wall along the left-hand side walking from Old Compton Street, as if there were no other businesses on this side of the road. This was of course the side of the Prince Edward Theatre. At the club we saw Jackson C. Frank, Bert Jansch, Davy Graham, Alexis Korner, Long John Baldry, Roy Harper, *et al*, as if we would never *not* see them. I will not forget the feeling of emerging from Cousins in the early dawn. Free soup at St Anne's, long walks home, laughing out of tiredness and the endless years of freedom ahead. Cousins was about ten shillings to get in, and there was no alcohol. Few music clubs were licensed then, and Cousins would certainly never have got its all-night music licence if it had been. Odd when you think that the basement was owned by the people who owned the restaurant upstairs, which was obviously licensed. People running clubs couldn't mess around with these laws.

An area where the squareness of the Cosmopolitans came in handy was the band jackets the group wore. When I first joined they had a set of jackets that had been made or bought around the time of the band's inception, 1959. They were a greyish blue gabardine in a box-cut drape with a long roll collar down to one button. They looked like something Lloyd Price or Little Richard would wear, and consequently I loved mine, and wore it out when I wasn't gigging with the band. We always wore our band jackets at gigs with black 'Como' ties that disappeared under the white collar of our shirts.

When it was decided to update the band look, a new set of jackets appeared from somewhere. These were a baby-blue three-button continental cut in a sort of brushed denim. Very modern. The reason I say these were useful was because at this time I was wearing pale blue jeans – a leftover from the ice-blue numbers we had worn with the Rocker gear. When worn together, the jacket nearly matched the jeans and looked like a brushed denim suit. I used to wear this ensemble to Cousins and looked like a refugee from Carnaby Street as I lay on the dusty basement floorboards and fell asleep during Roy Harper.

Chris and I used to walk all the way home to Croydon sometimes, falling about laughing most of the way. I've since gathered we were by no means alone. Many punters in those days in the West End would walk home in the early hours to their humble flats or their sleeping parents in the outer reaches of south or north London. Sometimes after Cousins, in the dawn hours before the Tube was running, we'd join the queue for free soup at St-Martin-in-the-Fields with the tramps, but more often we went to St Anne's in Soho.

There was this incredible woman who took care of all the waifs and strays in the early dawn of Soho, by the name of Judith Piepe. Judith, a big motherly German refugee who loved folk music and often put up homeless musicians at her Cable Street house in the East End, would invite people leaving Cousins to St Anne's in Dean Street for coffee until the Tube started running on Sunday mornings. She specialised in the homeless – her shelter in the basement of St Anne's church eventually became a homeless charity satirically called Centrepoint because the owners of the then-new office block on the Charing Cross Road found it more cost-effective to leave it empty than to rent it to tenants. Judith was a larger-than-life woman around whom many legends accumulated, one of which was that she had driven ambulances for the loyalists during the Spanish Civil War.

Paul Simon, who was thrown out of Cousins one night at the request of the organiser for singing badly and being boring, moved into the Cable Street house with his English girlfriend and lived with Judith for a short while in 1965. Paul had come over to England rather than wait for the American public's reaction to his and Art Garfunkel's first LP, released while he was in London. This was following in the footsteps of Bob Dylan, who had done the same thing in 1963. Simon played one night stands around Britain for most of that year and Judith heard him playing in the Flamingo club, an unusual venue for his act, and persuaded him to appear on a regular spot on a religious BBC show she introduced called *Five to Ten*. Because of this he was offered a contract by CBS and recorded *The Paul Simon Songbook*, originally only released in the UK, a solo acoustic session of songs, some of which became famous when re-recorded with Art Garfunkel. Judith also fixed up a one-off gig at St Anne's in July 1965 that featured Simon with a visiting Garfunkel and guest Jackson C. Frank.

It seems I had missed a New Year's Eve celebration in 1965. I had not yet fixed my flag to the new mast. Mick, Chris and several others jumped in the fountains at Trafalgar Square, the last year that would be lawfully possible. From there they all tramped to Les Cousins soaking wet, and watched Paul Simon in the early hours. Sounds like an anti-climax to me!

As for Cousins, which usually doubled its clientele around two in the morning with R&B musicians coming down to the cellar from the Flamingo and the Marquee, and wanting to hear some wizard acoustic players, its reputation grew unchecked during 1966–67. One amusing but telling story about the growing trendiness of the scene down there goes like this. In the summer of 1966 during an all-nighter featuring Alexis Korner, someone was talking to a couple of young women who had been at the evening session earlier featuring John Renbourn, brilliant guitarist and songwriter, sometime cohort of Bert Jansch, and asked them what they had thought of John. 'We were disappointed,' they replied. When the questioner retorted that he had heard that John was a great player, they replied, 'Oh, his playing was fine, but he wasn't as scruffy as we had hoped!'

The Cousins would not be permitted as a public venue today, as the only way in and out was by the stairs, and in the current nanny state the fire brigade would object to any licence application. Cousins had a large noisy fan as its only form of ventilation. Roy Harper once called for it to be to be turned off during his performance but some wit warned him that it wasn't a good move as it was the only fan he had in there. Did I mention Harper's long meandering instrumental pieces and dour demeanour?

The folk clubs had turned me on to country blues, but Mick Gibbs was already a huge fan and collector of pre-war blues. I went round to his parents' house a few times to listen to his LPs of lo-fi scratchy recordings of blues singers, and lent him my copy of John Mayall and Eric Clapton's *Blues Breakers*, which was *the* modern blues/club album. He dug it.

* * *

In September 1966, Chris and Mick left to hitch-hike around Germany. It seems someone had given Chris a parting gift of a huge joint to take with him. They actually got to an autobahn junction in Germany before retrieving it from their pack. At the same time a green-and-white police car started circling through the interchange complex with Mick and Chris in its sights. They dumped the joint quickly only to watch the police drive away, the joint irretrievable. They planned to get to India the following year but Chris didn't go. Mick got as far as Istanbul before ending up in prison with a couple of other Brits. They apparently were smoking something the authorities didn't approve of. Eventually the embassy got them out and they had twenty-four hours to leave the country and never return.

Chris and Mick's trip to Germany had been highlighted by a meeting with German pop star Drafi Deutscher, who had picked the boys up hitching and taken them to his home, giving them the full guest treatment. Upon learning Chris's surname, Drafi told them that he was due coincidentally to record some music at Lansdowne Studio in London early the following year, and that Chris should drop by. Chris took a note of the date. As the time came round, Chris enquired at Lansdowne, and was told that Drafi's session had been cancelled, and no more was known. We later learned that Drafi was in prison on drugs charges and had also been found guilty in 1967 of public indecency after he had urinated from a balcony while drunk, in plain view of a group of schoolchildren watching him from street level.

* * *

One night in late November 1966, after Mick and Chris had returned from their travels, all three of us were coming home from somewhere on the bus. Mick was wearing his 'Run Roberts Run' badge. This was the era of badges – the Americans called them buttons – with slogans on them. 'Make Love Not War' famously comes from this time. I can remember 'Johnson – The Bully With An Air Force', 'War Is Good Business – Invest Your Son', 'Psychiatry – The New Inquisition', 'Let's Legalize Love', and of course, 'Burn Baby Burn'. Then there were some fairly humorous items, like, 'Forget Oxfam – Feed Twiggy' or 'If It's Liquid – I Drink It'. The badges were inspired by the Situationists, the revolutionary organisation started by avant-garde artists in 1957 and very active in Europe in the sixties, and in whom Mick had taken an avid interest.

Mick's 'Run Roberts Run' badge referred to Harry Roberts, who had famously slain two coppers near Wormwood Scrubs in August 1966. Roberts had gone on the run, hiding out in woods using previous military training to survive, until he was caught and banged up forever in November. Although Roberts was already incarcerated by the time of our bus ride, the badge would continue to be worn by Mick in an encouraging gesture to Roberts (i.e. an aggressive snub to the police). Mick's badge got him stopped by the police *all the time*. We were on a demonstration together once and Mick got *special* treatment thanks to the badge. He was taken aside so we couldn't get involved, hassled and threatened for quite some time before being let go with a warning.

On the bus that evening, Mick was also carrying a copy of *International Times – IT* – one of the earliest issues, the first I saw.

None of us had seen anything like it. Being as I was a big blues freak, I perused an interview with Paul Butterfield and his band. I couldn't believe that the musicians were cursing in a published interview! And this was only the music section of the paper. It *had* to be Mick who would be hip to the UK's first underground press. He often spoke about the 'Anarchist Bookshop' up west. I'm not sure exactly what establishment Mick referred to as the 'Anarchist Bookshop', but it very well might have been Indica Books, which sat in Mason's Yard, near Leicester Square, and was next door to the Scotch of St James, another club. Barry Miles, usually known simply as Miles, friend of the Beatles, author, musician, book importer and art gallery manager, ran Indica, and it was there that John Lennon famously met Yoko Ono, during an exhibition of her art. As for Mick, he would become a man of letters in the years that followed, while Chris and I also got involved in underground publishing in the very early seventies.

Mick went on to university in Exeter and became a professor of English Literature at Amsterdam University. He would eventually have his own bookshop in Amsterdam. At Warwick Mick's English tutor was Germaine Greer, with whom he reputedly enjoyed heated differences of opinion. Greer would later feature in *Oz*, my favourite London underground magazine, and have books published that I would read in the coming decade. Mick was interested in visual poetry and published a magazine, *Kontexts*. He died in Amsterdam on 23 December 2009.

I never saw Mick again after some time in '67. It was only in recent years after Chris and I reconnected that he talked about trying to find Mick. Ultimately it would be too late. A Cousins/ Anarchy/Dada reunion would have been wonderful stuff.

Anarchy in the UK

I must mention that the first real underground paper we had ever seen was published by a man called Paul Pawlowski, a Polish anarchist who went on to form his own religion to escape prosecution for smoking hash. His magazine was called *Anarchy* (not to be confused with the magazine of the same name published by Freedom Press in London all through the sixties and into the seventies). Pawlowski's publication featured many Situationist-style sketches and was the forerunner to Jamie Reid's *Suburban Press* of the early seventies, itself the template for punk fanzines later on. During his *Suburban Press* days I would know Jamie and even write some stuff for his mag. As for Pawlowski, there are many stories, and I have no idea why he was in Croydon in the mid-sixties.

Chris had actually known Pawlowski for a while before I did. They had gone on a CND march together while Pawlowski was living in West Croydon. He would often give random people (usually female) bunches of flowers as he passed them. He also had the idea for limiting population growth – one woman to multiple husbands. His reasoning was that, rather than all those men getting so many women pregnant, one female would only be able to reproduce once a year despite having so many husbands. He also reasoned that so many 'bread-winners' would result in wealthier families. There was a letter published in the *Croydon Advertiser* suggesting that Paul go back to Poland if he was going to keep protesting in England. He accepted the challenge and went back to Poland, where he immediately started to protest about something and promptly got thrown back out.

He was one stage 'further out', so to speak, from even the 'genuine' Beats who frequented the scene. By which I mean, two steps away from 'Weekend Ravers'! If the Beats were authentic mainly because they smoked shit every day, were into be-bop rather than rock 'n' roll, did not work except for part time labouring, hung out in the Beat places – then Paul Pawlowski was *active*. He was, obviously, a real renegade from Poland.

I remember Pawlowski looking older than his years, physically a lot like Charles Bukowski. He seemed to be forever in court, and during appearances made a display of sitting on the floor and refusing to recognise the court. It made no difference to his conviction or sentence. His cases were mostly for possession of dope, although contempt of court might have been added. This eventually led him to create his own religion within which the smoking of dope was a sacrament. I can't remember if this worked, but he certainly ended up with his own religion and a church, the Temple of Aphrodite Pandemos. This was around the time, '66 and '67, that many fellows were claiming Rastafarianism as their religion so as not to have their hair cut upon remand. Not that it made any difference to their ability by law to smoke dope, which is ironic when you consider that in that religion smoking dope really is a sacrament. In any case, these were the times when arrest had become a real threat, and the days of quite openly taking a puff on quiet Croydon streets outside a pub were drawing to a close.

The magazine, *Anarchy*, left me with the biggest impression. It used images and ideas influenced by the Situationists, hence its sway over the Beat ethic. It must have had a profound influence on our friend Mick Gibbs.

Paul Pawlowski remained a mystery set in my own time until

I found out that he is still active, as is his church, both in publishing and in protest.

In 1965 Pawlowski published *Polyandry: the practice of one woman marrying a number of men*. Other examples of his numerous publications are: *The Fraud of Non-Violence*; *Problems of the Republican Party of England* and *Smash the Criminal Mafia in the British Medical Association*.

Students Are Revolting

Chris and I attended numerous demos between mid-1966 and early '67, at which we got very familiar with the squares, Trafalgar and Grosvenor. Actually the former acted on occasion as a large airy bedroom after an all-night club, these being the days before regular night buses. I was astounded the first time I awoke on a bench in Trafalgar Square to hear the loudest noise coming from thousands upon thousands of pigeons lining the rooftops around the square, screaming their morning chorus.

On 11 November 1965 the Rhodesian government under Ian Smith, defying British dictatorial rule, declared independence from Britain while retaining the Queen as the Head of State. Britain, in an act seen as betrayal by the 300,000 white Rhodesians who were almost all of British stock (and guaranteed entirely fascist bastards), retaliated by imposing sanctions that ensured Smith's Rhodesia was a renegade, pariah state. There was a Pink Floyd concert at the Albert Hall in December 1966 for Oxfam and related to Rhodesia. Duncan Sandys held a 'Peace with Rhodesia' rally in Trafalgar Square in January 1967, which was broadcast by the BBC. There was an enormous anti-Smith/Sandys turn-out. I wore an iron cross bought from Badges and Equipment in The Strand, the place where we had bought our 'Death or Glory' badges when we were Rockers. I got interviewed by an American TV crew, attracted to my Nazi insignia. They asked me if I was in agreement with the sanctions imposed on Ian Smith's regime. I may, I believe, have given them a confusing answer. Shit, I wore the iron cross because I'd seen it at Badges and Equipment and thought it was very cool. I wore it hung on a piece of string.

Rhodesia gained true independence and became Zimbabwe in 1980.

Blues Run the Game

So what about the group of people who Chris introduced me to? It included mainly upper-middle-class kids from good, often paying, schools. Our friend Hamish was one of them. His father was the most famous folk singer and writer of his generation, Ewan MacColl. This gave Hamish, at around fifteen, the licence to be a leader, be in the know, walk around in bare feet with a bottle of red wine, lend credibility to a local folk club with his presence. And chat up the nicest girls.

Pretty girls from good family stock were patently the main reason to be hanging out with this crowd. It was right at the beginning of these new days, at the first party that Chris took Alan and me to, that I met Rosalyn, easily the prettiest of the 'Beat girl' set, who introduced me to French kissing in the back of Alan's Minivan when we gave her a lift home. I was obsessed with her from then on, and spent a frustrating summer of '66 as she spent as much time with other blokes as she did with me. She wasn't into monogamy.

That party was at a friend of Rosalyn's, who lived a stone's throw from Hamish in Selsdon. Ritzy houses in private roads. Chris was in fact going out with Rosalyn, although he was probably about to end it since she also seemed to be going out with a queue of admirers, including a young guy called John Hobbs, who I was later to meet again. Oh yes, and Hamish. And a very talented guitarist called Pete Lieberman (who I've mentioned before). But that first party. Damn. Some of the women at the house were hanging out in their undies! Alan and I figured our quest had ended.

Around the corner at Hamish's house, where his famous dad no longer lived, we also attended some parties. One Christmas Chris and I popped in, in time for Robert Zimmerman to put a call through from the States. Did Bobby want to speak to Ewan? I expect so, but I don't remember. We dug the dulcimer, an Appalachian stringed instrument shaped like a woman, that 'Mish got from his dad for Christmas, and his kid sister, a precocious six year old named Kirsty, wanted to hang out and play with the boys. It would be some time before Kirsty would reappear in my life, seemingly a lifetime later.

The crowd encircling the Hamish/CND/folk scene was the crowd that met on Saturdays at the Whitgift gates and the Lyons. Then there was another part of this crowd, older, hairier, scarier. People with names like Meg, Smiler, Spade Alan, Pete Trimby. These guys were seriously into smoking dope and digging jazz. They were misfits, they followed no trend, they used the term 'Weekend Raver' to describe *anyone* who only smoked dope at weekend parties (hands up!), who had a job, had a haircut, shaved too often, who *believed* in anything. Meg squatted in a condemned water tower, Pete Trimby lived in a caravan deep in some woods somewhere surrounded by owls who had attacked him twice, and Smiler lived in a huge Edwardian house that had a small aeroplane half buried nose down in the vast back garden.

The first pub I was introduced to where these guys gathered was called the Telegraph, on Gloucester Road, Croydon. I *loved* this place. It had a tiny public bar where the obligatory men with cloth caps hunkered. One had to pass through this bar to get to a room the same size behind it. This was empty except for two wooden dining chairs with those loose round bottoms. Spade Alan seemed to live in that room, perched on one of the chairs while he drummed on the loose bottom of the other to the sounds coming from the Dansette record player, rigged up by these patrons who appeared to have an understanding with the landlord. During the warmer months that room could be empty except for Alan and his drum-chair and record player, always playing jazz. Beyond the back room was a yard, which was surrounded by a brick wall that separated it from a school playing field. In the yard was a tree in an untended garden, with a gravestone leaning precariously out of the ground. Around the gravestone were placed a few empty barrels that acted as seats. On these, around the anonymous grave, Chris and I would join this small unholy gang in getting plastered on cider or ale . . . with the occasional joint passed our way. The Telegraph was torn down shortly after these glory days and last time I looked was a flat piece of ground, giving the passer-by no indication that anything had ever been there.

The pub that took its place, with some little overlap, was the Royal Oak in Surrey Street, a public house that had once been attached to a brewery of the same name. This was the one that had 'Bird Lives' scrolled on the toilet door. In case you are wondering, that was an homage to Charlie 'Bird' Parker. In pre-'67 it had been fairly cool to smoke joints in the dark, empty street outside, where Croydon's only street market would be pushing cabbages and plastic buckets during the day. I say the Royal Oak was 'cool', but it did have enough underground activity going on to actually get raided. Chris had a lucky escape one night after seeing police vehicles parked up in a side street behind the pub when he was on his way there. His warnings at the pub went unheeded, and he moved on to the Gun Tavern. A few Royal Oak customers got hauled in that evening.

Neither the Telegraph nor the Royal Oak were where I was actually introduced to my first joint. This happened some weeks before my first visit to the Telegraph at a party in West Wickham, and although Chris and I were there, it seemed to be occupied by young people we were not familiar with. The parents had been away for about a year and the son was slowly taking the house apart. The banisters had been taken out to provide firewood. The police used to sit in a car down the road monitoring the place.

At some point we gravitated to an upstairs room and a bunch of guys kneeling around a fireplace. One of them had a measly lump of hash, and in his overly confident way of cooking the hash up over a flame in the fire, dropped it in. This resulting charred piece of black material was what we smoked in my first ever joint. One rather upper class chap standing nearby was offered it and spoke the immortal line, 'Thanks awfully, I'll stick to my Senior Service, if it's all the same.'

The feeling of breaking boundaries was more real than the actual imagined high we got off that piece of hash, which was more like ash. On our walk through the suburbs that night, Chris and I bounced with our own humour, making up for the serious amount of imagination needed to pretend we were stoned.

* * *

Our drug experience began with little 'quid deals' of hash, in a time of strict lines drawn in the world of recreational drugs. Since the early sixties we had heard and read about Purple Hearts, uppers, pills – speed, as they would generically become known. The first appearance of these pills to stray off the pages of the 'jazz parties' and 'pill parties' of the Sunday press, would be among the Mod kids we knew. Thing was, the pills were *their* drug. Consequently, we stayed 'clean' for just that bit longer, that is until we found ourselves in our own Beat world, and then – da dah! – a little bit of overcooked hashish.

In those days you didn't score hash from a 'real' drug dealer. You scored from someone you knew, and that person would have scored from someone who had bought, say, £10 worth (still a week's wages) from someone else. This would be divided into 'quid deals', but not evenly, as a £10 score was invariably divided into far more than ten individual quid deals. So although the law would view that seller as a dealer, he would actually be at the bottom of a very long chain. Back then the most common name for hash around our area was 'shit'. 'I've got a little bit of shit on me.' By the end of the sixties the name had morphed into 'charge', a mainly West Indian term, and more frankly descriptive.

Strict lines were drawn, though. Soon we would meet junkies. We knew an older woman (funny how we decided she wasn't a girl) called Junkie June. Everyone knew her, and knew her by her epithet. The drugs other people took did not influence us. We smoked pot, Mods took pills, junkies shot up heroin. June lived on our estate and I once found myself waiting round at her flat for something or other, on a day when she and a couple of her friends had taken delivery of their 'script. These three gals sat around on a *très ordinaire* council estate suite with needles full of their own blood, job half done, waiting for the right mix, talking about shopping. So incongruous and so off-putting. It all seemed to have more to do with hospitals than getting high. Times change, however, and in the years to come younger people than me would sadly fail to see the boundaries.

The Beat look, for me, sat between my Rocker look and the incoming psychedelic look. The main influences were always from up in town. People you would see in the *real* clubs and pubs of Soho, or stalking Portobello Road. I remember waistcoats being a big part of male attire around that time. I happened to have quite a collection, as sometime in the middle of '66, before Alan and I had started to hang out with Chris's people, I had gone through a period of trying to relive the Teddy boy era I had been born too late for. I had a dark blue wool suit made at Burton's, with sixteen-inch bottoms with turn-ups, fingertip length jacket, black velvet trim on the collar. My mate Alan almost refused to go out dancing with me, dressed as he was in the tonic mohair number he'd had made with side vents, the lot. I remember him saying the first night we got our suits delivered, 'I'm not going out with you in that, we'll get knifed.' Anyway, my Ted stage burned hot but briefly, it was so out of time. I just knew no other Teds. Plus this new Beat scene was grabbing my fancy. So now the waistcoats I had collected in my Beau Brummel-Ted period were getting dragged out to finish a casual shirt and Levi's look. Somehow I could not shake the old me. When I first met Rosalyn, for she was looming large in my focus on this scene, and I was trying damned hard to make her see that she belonged to me, she said, 'You're a bit of a Rocker boy, aren't you?' This was not the desired effect.

But I must mention one last piece, *the* last piece, of the sartorial puzzle from those times. There were these suede boots, coming, I think, from across the pond. They certainly seemed to adorn the feet of all the singer-songwriters from the States whichever way you looked. They were also hard to find here. They came up to mid-calf, with no zip, necessitating a real struggle to don them. Pale tan suede was the only colour they came in, with sturdy leather soles and heels, and round toes. They fit under your Levi's, and the ensemble gave you the total *effect*. You needed to get your boots worn in pretty quickly, to give a vague impression of travelling hard and scuffling a living. These suede boots became so *de rigueur* on the scene that in some small circles they acquired the name of 'pseudo boots'. Pronounced *suede*-o as in suede, or *pseudo* as in pseudo – please refer to 'Weekend Ravers' earlier. Someone, maybe Mick Gibbs, dubbed them finally '*per*suedo boots'. As in *The Persuaders*.

Portobello Road

Chris introduced me to Portobello Road late in September 1966. His purpose was to buy a guards' parade jacket, which were just gaining ground at the time; this was his consolation choice after an Afghan coat, which was too expensive. The establishment we were heading for sat at the rat's-ass northern end of Portobello, just past where the early excavations for the Westway had ravaged and scarred this part of 'The Lane'. This wasteland was nicknamed 'The Dark Side of the Moon' by Emily Young of 'See Emily Play' fame – Pink Floyd would make her and her title famous one day.

People set up stalls here selling tat in a less organised way than at the antiques end. 'I Was Lord Kitchener's Valet' was the name of a boutique that had opened that year specialising in antique military clothing like admirals' coats and guards' jackets. It proved to be popular with rock musicians and the set that dwelled in the grey area between Beats and Mods. It stood in the middle of a row of tumbledown terraced shops one block up from the overhead Metropolitan railway line that crossed over Portobello from east to west, and would one day soon be paralleled by the Westway. Chris bought a bright red number there, and he was as proud as Punch. On our way back along Portobello an old gentleman leaning on his front gate at one of those little cottages at the Notting Hill end of the road, where mostly old folks seemed to live (and which are now multi-million-pound merchant banker dwellings), started yelling at Chris that he shouldn't be wearing that jacket. He had fought in the Boer war or some other war, and was well cheesed off seeing his colours flaunted by a long-haired Beatnik like Chris.

This fell on one of the Saturdays when Alexis Korner ran his all-nighter, and so we were heading in that direction after getting something to eat and killing some time. Cousins was one of the only two clubs that stayed open all night in London at that time. 'The Cousins' was on Greek Street. The other one was The Flamingo on Wardour Street, where I had been to see Georgie Fame and the Blue Flames, but that was very much a Mod and Jamaican hang-out, while Cousins was a folk club, and therefore a Beat scene (it had been the Skiffle Cellar in the fifties). We liked to attend Alexis' nights, which would feature the likes of Roy Harper, Jackson C. Frank, the Spontaneous Music Ensemble (which was an improvising duo of drummer John Stevens and sax player Evan Parker), a harp player with shoulder-length red hair called Mox, the Incredible String Band, and any visiting Yanks that were passing through town, like members of the (then) 5th American Blues Festival, Little Brother Montgomery and Roosevelt Sykes. If you could stay awake all night, anything could happen.

By this time Alexis was experimenting with getting an electric three-piece together, influenced by the Cream, who had formed that summer. It was obvious that he wanted to form a kind of free-form blues trio, along the lines of the free-form jazz of the Spontaneous Music Ensemble. Well into the early hours of this particular morning in September, some interesting-looking types arrived at the club and were hanging out while a buzz went around that there would be a jam coming up. After either a short break, or perhaps a sleep-inducing Roy Harper instrumental opus, Alexis climbed onto the little stage with some guests. One of these guests stood out. He was black (we somehow inferred he was also a visiting Yank), wore a ragged raincoat, and was hoisting an electric bass upside down around his neck to play left-handed. The following 'blues' jam was pretty wild, but mainly because this 'bass player' played more lead guitar on the bass than Alexis was playing on his guitar, which was not hard to do, but was unheard of, especially at Cousins. I can't even remember who else was playing, but I think Victor Brox was singing. Raincoat man left an impression.

In the following couple of months, Alexis developed his trio at Cousins, calling it Free At Last. He featured a black bass player called Binkie McKenzie, and, together with drummer Hughie Flint, they started gigging around the country. We saw them later at the Star Hotel. Chris and I always assumed that Binkie was the black bass player we had seen sitting in with Alexis that night. It didn't dawn on me until years later that Binkie was *right-handed*. The man we'd seen that night at Cousins was Jimi Hendrix. But by the way, Binkie was a fucking fabulous bass player.

Just after Christmas '66 we all saw the Jimi Hendrix Experience on *Top of the Pops* doing 'Hey Joe'. I thought, this is wild, a black guy with a Dylan hairstyle playing a Strat upside-down. I had seen some posters around London billing the Jimi Hendrix Experience. It was an era of quirky names for groups. We had seen Them, we had seen the Who. So this new name fitted into that angle of strange names. After this things moved fast. On a Monday in February of the following year Jimi appeared at the Star Hotel, and blew the minds of an audience the size of which is hotly contested but, either way, was *small*, with the help of his Experience, Mitch and Noel. And for years I thought that was the first time I had seen Jimi Hendrix. Until decades later, while reading an Alexis Korner biography, it transpired that Chris and I, and a few others, had seen him that night in September '66 down at Cousins, just after his arrival in London!

That night at the Star in February 1967, he climbed on stage wearing a wrestler's satin cape, doffed it, and beneath it he was wearing a black guards' jacket. And where had he bought it? At I

Was Lord Kitchener's Valet. As much as I'd love to think that Jimi's jacket was from Portobello Road, in fact the branch he shopped at was on Old Compton Street at the corner with Wardour Street, the first West End outlet for the business, located to catch the crowd going to and returning from the Marquee Club. Many other members of the rock fraternity (it wasn't quite 'royalty' then) bought their versions at Portobello, like Mick Jagger. Oh, and Jimi's had a sleeve half hanging off.

Chris and I had got quite pally with Alexis, and the first time Free At Last played at the Star Binkie McKenzie put me and Chris on the guest list. We were among a group rapping in the saloon bar with Korner. The talk of the town was Jimi Hendrix, and Chris asked Alexis what he thought of the man setting light to the London scene. Alexis was quite dismissive of any accolades, preferring to measure his own opinion about Jimi's talents, and even saying, 'Oh, he'll get better, but he's not quite there yet,' in that lovely smoked posh voice, that anyone who had spent time rapping with Korner would instantly recognise. Funny what you remember. And at the time we still had no idea we'd seen the great man himself a few months before his Star appearance. Old Korner was not one for being upstaged and then forgetting.

On Bert's Passing

Bert Jansch, who died on 5 October 2011, had a larger influence on rock (and a generation) than most people realise. If one had listened to Bert earlier in the sixties, upon hearing 'Black Mountain Side' on the first Led Zep LP, one said, 'Oh, that's Bert.' The tune 'Angie' was his main theme – not because he wrote it, that was Davy Graham, the grand master of acoustic blues guitar at the time – but because Bert played it with a certain fire and made it his own.

Every young guitar slinger on the folk scene tried his hand at 'Angie', as if it were a necessary addition to his credentials, like notches on a gun butt. We had our own guy, Dave Eggert, who played a pretty good version, and always seemed out of his mind, which added to his cred. Everyone knew Bert's 'Angie' was the best – witness the version on Simon & Garfunkel's first album after Simon's time soaking up the scene around Soho. Even though everyone knew Davy Graham had written the tune, and could also be seen in and around the clubs performing regularly, he exuded a certain cool that extended to his singing, which left some listeners cold.

Bert's rough edges were what won his following, and his rendition of Davy's piece was definitive. Oddly, it was the cerebral and haughty Graham who was the heroin addict while Bert may have smoked hash like everyone else, his shyness hidden behind alcohol was what made him seem more vulnerable than his young years allowed. The song 'Needle of Death' on his own first album, although a warning against the drug and based on a friend's death, seemed to tie him into a hard drug culture, when in fact he was singing against it.

While we saw the heroes of the sixties folk scene at Cousins, they also appeared at local clubs like Under the Olive Tree, the Star Hotel, the Gun Tavern and the Bridge. Bunjies, which was on Litchfield Street, up west, and had all the usual suspects appearing there, was all right, but always felt secondary to Cousins. We all found ourselves from time to time at Ewan MacColl's Singers Club, at whatever address it was residing at the time, but the vibe there was strict and lacked humour. Of the two warring factions in folk music, Bert Jansch was a reluctant leader and innovator of the progressive, while at the Singers an artist would be disallowed to sing a song of American origin if he or she did not at least hail from Canada! Also, of course, Ewan's club was very communistic, and humour played very little part in the proceedings.

The Beat scene for my circle consisted of young suburbanites who were drawn to the rebellious and subcultural world of 'protest' songs, the blues, all-night clubs, quid deals of hash scored from a friend who scored it from a 'real' Beat, who scored it from a Jamaican acquaintance, and seemingly endless females on a mission to end their virginity (who of course were on the scene for all the previous reasons too). Oh yeah, and we also enjoyed a pretence at intellectualism, ranging from the books we read to the art we liked to the politics we veered towards, as the Vietnam war took us to Grosvenor Square.

Saturday would find a bunch of us gathered at East Croydon station. A ritual where someone would let us know where 'the party' was. If it was local we would spend the next few hours in a 'friendly' pub and then head to the address. If it was up in town we could get straight on the train there and then. Someone would let you know quietly who had some hash. Often there would be a rumour about Bert Jansch turning up at the party. There must have been parties the man went to, of course, but I was never at one. I was once at a party where Jackson C. Frank played, though.

A baby
boom family.

First bicycle.
Count the cars.

Fifties caravan holiday.

Mum (*left*), me & aunty
Evelin. Touring London
in the early fifties.

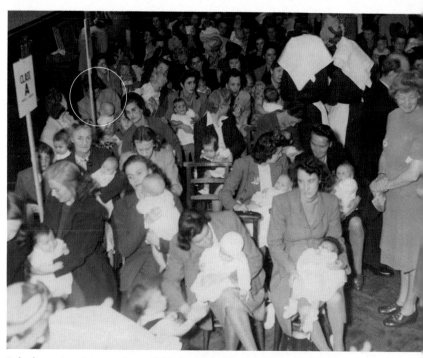

Baby boom mothers at a beautiful baby show. Me & Mum circled.

Seventeen.

Rockers 1964.
Chris Lansdowne on
the left, me on the right.
Pete Bruce behind the
wheel in both.

Tina, Easter 1964.

With Mum age thirteen.

Demob Dad.

Dave James at my front door with my fencing foil 1963.

Kathy and me – Mods & Rockers in love 1964.

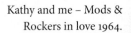

My minimal kit getting ready to play some trash 1963.

Graveyard pose – not sure which style direction to take 1963.

The Classics.
L-R: Nicky, Tony,
Dave & me 1963.

The Cosmopolitans
1965. Ron Diamond
sitting, me on
the right.

The Blues
Brothers;
me sporting
a borrowed
Madras jacket
1967. L-R: Me,
Will, Roger,
Rick, Tony.

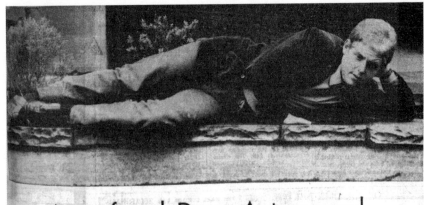

A confused Dave Antony and the case of a handful of pop groups he has known

MOST people have heard of the Riot Squad, some of the League of Gentlemen, and quite a few of Dave Antony and the Moods.

But when I met Dave Antony himself the other day he was a very confused young man.

It seems that he is, or was, part of all of these groups at one time or another, and that at the moment he is the singer with yet another group—Dave Antony and the Anzacs.

He told me that the Riot Squad, a group which made quite a name for itself and yet failed to have a hit, is now being disbanded. At the moment, however, Dave is still with the group.

He went on to explain that the Riot Squad also went under the name of the League of Gentlemen. They used this name when appearing as a backing group for well-known artists like Lee Dorsey and Don Covay.

But now it seems that both the Riot Squad and the League of Gentlemen are dead and that they have been reincarnated as Dave Antony and the Anzacs.

Dave told me that the new name for the group was intended to be the Moods—until they found out that the name was already being used by another group.

By the time he had finished telling me this story I was even more confused than he was, so I changed the subject and asked him about himself.

Dave's real name is Dave Imber, and he is an 18 year old who lives at Chesney Crescent, New Addington.

On leaving school his ability on the guitar resulted in a job with Rolf Harris' backing group, the Diggeroos.

The group disbanded, so Dave decided to form his own, the Moods. While he was with them he toured Germany and did a six month stint in Copenhagen.

Popular group

After a while, though, he left the Moods. A spell as lead singer with the popular Croydon group the Trees followed, and then he joined the Riot Squad, which at this time consisted of members of a former Liverpool group, the Anzacs.

Under the name of the Riot Squad, Dave and the group made a record. The disc, says Dave, was "lousy" and "died a natural death"—and prefers the name of the record to remain forgotten.

But he is enthusiastic over the future of the Anzacs, of which he is also lead singer.

He has a trip to Copenhagen lined up for this month and on July 4 the group are to have a record issued. The new disc, "Here Babe," was written by Dave himself. He has high hopes for its success.

In between times, Dave is not forgetting his home ground. On Sunday the group will play at New Addington's weekly dance—Sunday Spin.

NICK COBBAN

Dave James makes the local press. Croydon Advertiser June 1966.

Chris Lansdowne and Françoise Hardy! A demonstration at Trafalgar Square c. 1965. Chris was singled out to pose with Françoise, while I stood with the photographer.

© Jours de France

Chris Reeves with his LD Lambretta 1965.

Chris Lansdowne & me with our bikes 1965. With bleached out L plate.

Chris Lansdowne on the
road near Köln 1966.
Picture taken by Mick Gibbs.
© Chris Lansdowne

Rosalyn sports the bike
and sandals look.

Me at the Coal 'Ole 1967.

A looning Chris Reeves, sporting double Madras, in the back room of the Dog & Bull, with 'Beat' clientele.

Pub customers' move to put curb on drugs

CUSTOMERS of a Croydon publican advertised in the underground Press urging youngsters not to cause trouble by taking drugs into the public-house.

This was stated at Croydon Magistrates' Court on Wednesday when the licensing justices renewed the licence of The Star, London Road, Broad Green, for a further 12 months.

Two weeks ago the application was adjourned for further consideration when the police reported that warrants to enter The Star had resulted in 12 persons being charged with possessing cannabis.

Mr Martin Larcombe appearing for the joint licensees, Mr and Mrs Albert Smythe, and the brewers, Courage, said the Smythes had been tenants of The Star for 22 years with no previous trouble.

In the latter part of 1970 it came to the Smythes' attention that various customers were suspected of possessing drugs.

They asked for police advice and consulted their customers, with whom they were on extremely good terms.

Barred

It was then that the customers put the announcement in the underground Press, said Mr Larcombe.

But subsequently there were three police raids on the premises and 12 people were charged with drugs offences.

Mr Larcombe said that all the customers involved in the offences had been barred from the public-house and a clubroom was closed. The brewers were now satisfied that there was no further danger of drugs offences on the premises.

Mr Smythe told the court that from the beginning they had employed extra staff whose duty was to watch out for any recurrence of this trouble.

New image

Mrs Smythe said the clubroom had been a meeting place for youngsters.

"We now want to give the pub a new image," she said. "As long as we or any other pub have youngsters as customers we will have this problem."

My rip-off from
Robert Crumb.

Illustration by
Jeff Willard.

White Panthers in IT:
L-R: Jeff Willard, Jeff Tree, John
Carding & me 1972.

Brian Nevill

Brian Nevill
is an accredited representative of

FRENDZ

Editor

PRESS

'Music for the People, Pigfucker!'

Freak workers at a national record distribution firm, pissed-off at wholesale sackings & a management-inspired informers' network, are starting to hit back. The company   concerned is Phonodisc – owned by Phillips but handling albums & tapes for CBS, Pye, Atlantic, Liberty, Island, Warner/Reprise, etc, It's a firm that is staffed largely through casual labour, recruited from an agency called Mills Enterprises. Because of the ready availability of staff, the turnover of employees is high, and Phonodisc don't seem to be too worried about how they treat their workers.

Obviously, in a company dealing with records, staff rip-offs are quite common. Like virtually every record company in Britain, Phonodisc lose albums regularly, but their efforts to stop this go much further than most. They've got an ex-CID man – ironically called Kinder who they hired from Scotland Yard to head their security force, and according to sources within the firm, he's just as piggish as ever.

His security force has instigated a number of sly little practices – like putting up notices asking full-time staff to grass on the temps if they think they're ripping-off albums, asking them to go up to new staff and ask if they can score, and generally inducing a paranoid atmosphere.

Kinder co-operates with the pigs – 20 people have been busted in the last month, and homes are frequently searched. One guy – a spade – apparently got 3 years for nicking seven Woodstock albums, and there have been other cases of people going down for small thefts.

Another of Phonodisc's little tricks was to sack 35 temps (wage 10/- per

hour) and replace them with students (6/- per hour). When the students went back to college, Phonodisc hired another set of temps   from the agency.

It's obvious that the security force runs the firm. Our informant says that several people have been sacked simply because Kinder and his goons don't like them. But the employees are hitting back. They've had stickers made – "Music for the People, Pig-fuckers" and "Show us your balls, Phonodisc" – and these are being put into parcels of records just before they're sent out to shops.

We contacted Phonodisc for their side of the story. The man in charge of personnel, Mr Parks, wasn't there, but after a long wait and signs of great agitation at the other end – "Somebody's got to talk to him . . . he says he's from Informational Times" . . . his secretary told us: "Actually, I think you've got the wrong end of the stick. Our security force is very good – they wouldn't do anything like that." When told that we had a copy of one of the notices about informing (smuggled out by one of the employees), she added hastily, "Well, maybe you'd better phone back and speak to Mr Parks. He'll be here tomorrow, or maybe the day after."

Just after speaking to her, we had another call from another employee, telling us that another 33 were sacked on the previous Friday – again with no reason given.

When we finally got through to Parks, he transferred the call to Mr E A Muxlow – the man who signed the notices. He denied everything, and said that our informants must have worked for another firm, pointed out that "one doesn't sack temporary staff, anyway", and then said, "Look, I'll have to call you back, our Chairman's on the line from Stockholm." We're still waiting.

I QUIT !

① By the looks of the new issue no-one on this paper gives a shit, but there was a time when some of us cared.

③ All those that used to care have gone.

③ There is no room for fresh ideas — the mag is counter-productive. No-one's articles or reviews get published unless they're well known (thanx!)

④ I'm pissed off with never seeing anyone in this office.

⑤ I want nothing to do with the con disguised as a new issue.

⑥ I don't know who to address this to, 'cos no-one seems to exist anymore.

⑦ Someone else can finish off the mail order donkey work.

⑧ The only thing I gained was a cuppla frendz and a nick-name.

BIG BRIAN.

Frendz resignation.
Courtesy John May

Press card

ATLANTIS NEWS AGENCY
Telephone 01-460 9697

Brian Nevill

This is to certify that
Brian Nevill

is our reporter

Demo against the Kentish Independent 1972. L-R: Me, Linda, Jeff Willard, unknown women, Jeff Tree, John Carding, Rob Warr.

As above. Jeff Tree in foreground, me in leather hat.

Peoples Association Food Programme

As an extension of the White Panther Party Free Food Programme and as a move towards the formation of a food co-operative in West London, deals will be available at the Peoples Association, 10 Talbot Rd, W.8. First week commencing Sat. Nov 28, from 3 p.m. onward. These consisting of rice, vegetables, bread, butter and tea at 12½ a.t. We hope to continue at least this means of support is adequate. Any money made will be returned to the community. Programme of some stages. Accounts will be published irregularly in the underground press. Being open daily except when free food is available from White Panthers.

"Come enjoy our food around a nice cosy fire."

All Power to the People.

White Panthers give a free 'eat-in' every week

FREE FOOD is being given out once a week in the Portobello Road by the West London Chapter of the White Panther Party.

Last Friday at 3.30 p.m. was the fourth time the group of young people met under the motorway armed with table, gas rings, giant saucepans and paper cups to feed the people.

Children gathered round as the rice and vegetables were cooking and passers-by came up almost suspiciously to see what was going on.

The food is for anyone who needs it — and the Panthers work on the assumption that unless somebody is authentically hungry, they won't swallow their pride so much as to ask for food.

But operating under the motorway has its problems, not least of them being the cold and the fact that maybe the people who need the food most couldn't stand about in the queue waiting for it.

Their aim is to get a base indoors where they could also have a free school, yoga and karate classes, a poster workshop and an office for their magazine "White Trash."

The initial money to get the food programme off the ground came from Oz and from two pop groups, Hawkwind and The Pink Fairies. The equipment was donated by IT, the Magic Carpet and others.

"But we need help to keep the programme together, like free transport, sources of cheap or free food, disposable cups and containers, and help with the cooking and carrying of equipment," said a spokesman. The White Panthers can be contacted at International Times.

● (BELOW) KIDS swarmed around a table under the motorway in the Portobello Road last Friday, attracted by the smell of cooking. The food is being given away by the West London Chapter of the White Panthers. (K18,19)

Under the Westway. I'm on the left.

Linda on Tavistock Road.

Alan Male at Tavistock Road.

The In Crowd – A Piece About Togs

Mohair Sam was a hippy who was 'happening all over town' in Charlie Rich's hit song. The lyrics to Charlie's song beg the question of when the word 'hippy' was first used, and what it meant in 1965.

When it was used to describe Flower Children in 1967, they themselves, and the whole scene or generation of heads, freaks and post-Beats, definitely never used the term. In the latter part of the sixties it started to get used as a self-deprecating and good-humoured joke, or as an insider jest. Or even as a resigned denial, as in, 'I'm just a hippy, why do you want to pick a fight with/search/blame/arrest me?'

Going back to the forties there had been hipsters. Hipsters seemed different from the later Beats – they seemed more like the early Mod(ernist)s, ironically. As in sharp 'continental' suits in deference to black modern jazz musicians, and a 'cool' attitude, whereas the Beats seemed to emerge wholesale after 1957, with the publication of *On The Road*, wearing berets, goatees and sandals (can't afford the scandal). The only two things the Beat and hipster seemed to have in common were the perennial dark eyewear and the following of be-bop jazz. Then there were the actual images of the guys and gals who were the stars of the Beat Generation ten years before publication: Kerouac, Cassidy, Ginsberg, *et al.* Their preferred mode of dress seems to have been T-shirts and Levi's. The original Beats actually *looked* like Rockers! Sartori for the satori?

And there is also a correlation between the early Mods and the Beats of the late fifties/early sixties in the UK. Travel back in time, if you will, to Eel Pie Island in Twickenham, that London suburb sitting in the Thames delta, on the nights when the first jazzers in residence gave way to the early rhythm and blues mayhem of Alexis Korner's babies, the Rolling Stones. Check out the audience. All Boho chic, the duffle coat and corduroy brigade, with a few Mods dressed down for the occasion.

If you will excuse my borrowing a few quotes, the first listing of the word 'hipster' is in the short glossary 'For Characters Who Don't Dig Jive Talk,' which was included with Harry the Hipster Gibson's 1944 album, *Boogie Woogie in Blue*. The entry for 'hipsters' defined them as 'characters who like hot jazz'. Initially, hipsters were usually middle-class white youths seeking to emulate the lifestyle of the largely black jazz musicians they followed. In *The Jazz Scene*, published in 1959, Eric Hobsbawm (writing under the pen name Francis Newton) described hipster language, i.e. 'jive-talk' or 'hipster-talk', as 'an argot or cant designed to set the group apart from outsiders'. It was a veritable subculture that rapidly expanded, and after the war a burgeoning literary scene grew up around it.

Kerouac described 1940s hipsters as 'rising and roaming America, bumming and hitch-hiking everywhere [as] characters of a special spirituality'. In his essay 'The White Negro', Norman Mailer characterised hipsters as American Existentialists living a life surrounded by death, 'annihilated by atomic war or strangled by social conformity', and electing instead to 'divorce [themselves] from society, to exist without roots, to set out on that uncharted journey into the rebellious imperatives of the self'.

Mezz Mezzrow, in his book published in 1946 called *Really the Blues*, included a glossary of terms to explain the slang used in the book. The definition of *Hipster* here is: 'man who's in the know, grasps everything, is alert. *Hip*: in the know, worldly-wise, clever, enlightened, sophisticated'.

Really the Blues was published in paperback by Corgi in 1961. This is the printing I first read. I seem to remember it being on sale in the publishers' remainders bin in our local Woolworth's. This must have happened no later than 1962. It crystallised in my mind. It confirmed for me so many things I wanted to follow, do, be. Doo Bee Doo. I spent months speaking only in jive talk at school.

So, in spring '66 I became a Beat. At least that's what the kids were calling themselves at the time I reconnected with Chris, and dumped my dandy Ted apparel for the time being. So in quick succession I'd gone from Rocker to Ted to Beat. This would mean shopping for clothes at I Was Lord Kitchener's Valet and the Swap Shop, our very own military surplus shop. The Swap Shop, which also sold toys, electric trains, second-hand musical instruments, cameras, navy kit, fishing tackle, swords and guns (!), was in a back street behind Kennards department store in Croydon, now gone and replaced by a huge shopping horror called Centrale, or something like that.

Kennards had a famous exotic arcade running right through it on the ground floor, with pony rides for the kids, something my parents had treated me to in the fifties. The rides were always called donkey rides, but the hapless creatures were, in fact, ponies. The arcade included Asian shopkeepers who sold incense, never heard of, or smelled, by us before. There was a big old jukebox that played 78s. The arcade was a wondrous place. The Swap Shop was where Chris and I had bought studs for our Rocker gear, and now we could buy ex-military clothing which we were getting into. I got a really nice leather flying jacket with a fake fur collar.

Lord Kitchener's stock was quite Mod, in fact, in a King's Road Mod way, in as much as King's Road types were wearing the guards' jackets all over town, including Mick Jagger and Eric Clapton. Everywhere around the West End you could find these postcards for sale, created by some London artist, of 'Beatniks'.

They were crudely drawn cartoons, insulting, though funny, brightly coloured; the figures always had flies buzzing around them. Quite often they would be dressed in guards' jackets *à la* Lord Kitchener.

By 1967 the Beat look was morphing. I was into psychedelic shirts and granny glasses – you know, the round wire frame jobs – with a two-inch white leather jeans belt and sneakers. I had a shirt where the fabric was printed with a photograph of seashells, and then dyed a deep burgundy. Later that year I acquired a green satin job with an elongated collar with rounded ends, which I wore with skinny pullovers 'borrowed' from my aunty and mum. These type of shirts had actually originated with John Stephen on Carnaby Street; everyone else ripped off the idea. This look later morphed into a parallel trousered and white slip-on look, the trousers being of a basic colour, like green or mustard, sharply pressed with no turn-ups, the slip-ons from Raoul's, which were a copy of American Florsheims.

How and when the Beat look, motivation and idealisation morphed into the 'freak' lifestyle I could not say. But it seemed to be no time at all before one could smoke pot and listen to jazz and underground LPs, while actually looking any way one wanted. No uniform necessary.

Dust My Blues

I had joined the Bridge Folk Club in August 1966. The club was good for a number of reasons. Meeting girls was one, hearing good music was another. For me what you heard on the folk scene in those days divided into three catagories. One was the pure English, Irish or Scots folk, often sung unaccompanied, with a whiney twangy accent and interminably long songs. This I found a little sleep-inducing. Then there was the category of young singer-songwriters, the sort of guest who would sing Dylan songs or his or her own compositions. I placed the Jackson Franks, Jansches and Al Stewart in this bag, and I quite liked them. The third branch would be unadulterated blues. This included finger-style guitar pickers, wailing harmonicas and dusty boots. I tolerated even the more mediocre versions in this category. Even up at Cousins I had noticed that there were some codes to this. If a guitarist played a six-string guitar he or she would play like Big Bill Broonzy. If a twelve string was employed the influence would be Leadbelly. The harp players tended to worship Blind Sonny Terry or Noah Lewis from the thirties. They all shunned the electric style of Little Walter so popular in the R&B clubs of the time.

On the ground floor of the Bridge Hotel there was a small anteroom to the left of the stairs that led up to the club room. This room just had tables and chairs in it, and on folk nights would be used as a hang-out before, during and after the club. Musicians would spend time there, playing guitars and swapping stories and phone numbers, whether they were performing upstairs that night or not.

In January 1967 I quit the Cosmopolitans, my 'wedding' band. I had become increasingly frustrated with the fact that what I played was no longer the music I listened to at home and at clubs, which by then was the blues. So off I went in search of a blues band. It was February when I met Roger Hudspith, a young sharp-looking Mod type, in the downstairs room at the Bridge. We talked about getting a blues band together. He told me he knew a guy who played guitar as good as Eric Clapton, and that we should form a band round him. Well, that room at the Bridge was full of guys who 'played as well as' Eric Clapton – that is, the ones who didn't play as well as Bert Jansch, or as well as Davy Graham, or as well as whoever.

The band started rehearsing at Roger's parents' house in Norbury. He had got all the guys together, and they were all strangers to me. The talented and much-touted guitarist was Rick, of lanky frame and orange flaxen hair, the bass player was called Paul, a somewhat scruffy guy who turned out not to fit in too well, and there was a harmonica player called Will, who was very young, extremely tall, a student at the posh Whitgift Trinity School in the centre of Croydon. Will and I were to become good friends. Roger was meant to be our manager, but a serious lack of a lead vocalist placed him in the role of singer. He was not a good singer, but he managed to rasp out a blues repertoire with enough aplomb to escape critical audience attention.

Our name was going to be the Blues Brotherhood, which was my idea, until we found the name had already been appropriated. So we shortened it to the Blues Brothers, which was not as good, but it stuck. Yes, I was in a band called the *Blues Brothers* in 1967, more than a decade before Belushi and Aykroyd!

Our main gig was an interesting place in the Addiscombe area of East Croydon: a building owned by the Toc H charity organisation, sitting in a line of terraced houses, and called, in *yoof* club tradition, the Coal 'Ole. One entered the Coal 'Ole through a large front door that opened into a spacious hall. A desk would be set up at the top of a flight of stairs which led down to the cellar. The cellar had the obligatory table tennis and the like, and some nice little nooks and crannies dotted about, perfect for snogging purposes. This may very well have once been the coal cellar for the house. Back up another flight of stairs one came out into the garage at the side of the house. The garage had a soft drinks bar along one wall, and at the end by the garage doors the group would set up. There was no stage as such. The walls were covered with LP sleeves, the room got jammed, and the walls and everyone between them sweated away happily.

The Blues Brothers became regulars at the Coal 'Ole on Monday nights. By April, Paul, who was never really into the spirit of the thing, always wanting to do Stones covers and not authentic blues stuff, failed to return from a trip with the merchant navy. Rumour had it that he had ended up in prison somewhere in Africa. The new bass player we recruited was my old mate Tony Perry, who I had not seen since the Dave James German-gig fiasco of the previous year.

The Coal 'Ole gigs were attended by some old faces, like Storine, the girl singer from the Cosmopolitans; various local musicians; and the Saturday residency was held by a great combo named Formula Four, the newest incarnation of Glen and Holly, our old friends from the Nesters. Their singer was Ruby James, who went on to become a professional singer and recording artist later. It had been Ruby who had connected Chris back with Holly. He had, in fact, become Formula Four's roadie. It was a good little scene at the Coal 'Ole, with everyone turning out to see everyone else's group. Formula Four appeared on *Opportunity Knocks* and drew a capacity crowd to the club.

It was during this time that Chris and I became familiar with another kind of 'blues'. 'Blues' parties. We were first introduced to them by a young West Indian guy called Prince, who had named himself after Prince Buster. He was a fellow worker at the RAC, a job that Chris had arranged for me and that I had been working beside him at since early 1967. The 'blues' were essentially south London happenings in private houses, spread over all the floors of the house, strictly West Indian revellers apart from us and some dubious-looking white women; beans and rice being served on cardboard plates; ska records blasting and copious amounts of grass.

Eventually Rick from the Blues Brothers took me to a few of these parties too. There was a Jamaican guy called Johnny who lived at Selhurst, and he would throw his whole house open to a party, all three floors. Rick and his friends scored hash from Johnny, so that was how we got invited. By now the hash we were scoring was a vast improvement on the charred lump of the previous year! Johnny was a blues fan, that is the Albert King/Freddy King kind of blues. What Johnny's guests were dancing to they called blues, the Prince Buster and Skatalites type blues. What we were digging they would call rhythm and blues, or plain 'old' music. We would sit in his bedroom at the top of the house and he would spin a few of the latest blues singles, records you wouldn't get to know were released in England unless you happened to hang around Dobell's or the Swing Shop in Streatham a lot. Downstairs Prince Buster or the Skatalites would be pumping for the dancers, while we grooved to Albert King and Johnny's charge. Sometimes a young family member, like a teenage niece, would pop her head around the door to ask something of Johnny, and say, 'Uncle John, why you gotta play that old-time music?'

She probably went back downstairs and said, 'Why has Uncle John got those weird white boys sitting around in his bedroom?'

* * *

The Blues Brothers got engagements all around south London and as far afield as Brighton, but never went north of the River. I met my new girlfriend, Desiree, at the Bridge Folk Club, very early in '67, and we had our first date at the Coal 'Ole. Mick Gibbs introduced us, as he was going out with one of her mates. In the cellar of the Toc H house she told me she was fourteen (uh-oh), but she would be fifteen really soon! I seem to remember she was an April child, so her birthday was soon after.

Desiree attended Croydon High School for Girls, which was a pretty swanky school. Like her school mates she was as fashionable as she was of higher than average IQ. Mini-skirts and a taste for the arts had me trotting along behind her to galleries and the theatre. Desiree would ask me why I was so laconic, she encouraged me to engage. I'd had no idea I was so lacking in communication skills till then.

Croydon girls, like Croydon boys, divided into recognisable types. What was left of the distaff side of the Mod movement were 'moddy' girls. Working class, neatly dressed, good dancers, but only in it until they got hitched. Their older sisters had started the whole style revolution, but the younger siblings were simply girls with quite nice jobs, 'boutique' clothes and layers of make-up. They probably went to Tiles, the once-fashionable underground club situated at the eastern end of Oxford Street, famous for all-day record sessions and being open at lunchtime for teens that worked in town, or wished they did. They would be the equivalent of the 'moddy' boys we had met at Windsor. Our mates who were willing to stay in New Addington went out with these girls while I had moved on to the girls from Croydon High School!

On the Beat scene, which seems to have included girls from good homes exclusively, yet stretched to include working-class boys, we had plenty of chances to meet girls from very affluent homes, rich bored darlings who ended up doing rather all right for themselves, usually by marrying well after tiring of the 'scene', or else went right off the deep end and fucked themselves up.

But this lot from Croydon High, they were from parents who had made good solid money by doing good solid jobs and could pay for the privilege of good schooling and all the mini-skirts they could buy from the King's Road. Their parents were from the medical and teaching professions, or were small business owners. But their daughters longed to be in that other group, the lot with so much money they were bored with it.

Then there was another group, very prevalent on the scene, who could often actually be from either of the previous two groups, but never from the 'moddy' lot. These were the intellectual girls, scruffy ban-the-bombers who liked Indo-jazz fusions, who read Baudelaire and scowled at anything as mindless as being 'trendy', which was anything from any of the other groups. Rosalyn, who I had been so hung up on, and would meet again later, fitted into this group. But it was Desiree who dragged me up to the King's Road, as well as to highbrow events like modern ballet and art house cinema. Meanwhile me and Chris were the chaps from the wrong side of town. The deal was that a frankly under-educated chap with the right attitude could be found in the company of any of the above, which was an okay deal as far as Chris and I were concerned.

Will from the Blues Brothers started going with another of Desiree's friends from school, and one fine day in the spring the four of us were relaxing in the public gardens by the side of Croydon Technical College, right near Fairfield Hall. We were getting carried away with the petting scene, although there's not much you can *really* do in a public open space. Anyway, some old biddy who had been sitting in the park thought we'd gone too far and called the police. The first I knew of it was when the back of my head was being sniffed by a police dog. We were surrounded. The four of us were taken to Croydon nick. It was here that it was discovered that the girls were fifteen, Will was sixteen, and I was an old man of nineteen. So the other three were minors and had to have their parents called in, and I, so they told me, should have known better. We were separated. The two girls were given a grilling by some particularly nasty policewomen, and when their parents got there they were advised that a carnal knowledge test would be advisable. The point was, no sexual law had been broken. Nor had anything else. Will's girlfriend's father was a councillor or someone very important, and the police were told to back off. All the parents of this little lot had money and power. Consequently, however, I was warned to stay away from Desiree, or she would be made a ward of court.

We stayed together, and it didn't end until the summer. Our secret affair was only discovered after I had dumped poor Desiree with a ceremonious and gauche letter, leading to her parents finding out. She caught hell from her mother, and I got a lecture from her, too. She was, however, still a virgin.

Two years later she would seek me out, seemingly to finish what we'd begun.

Shoot the Moon

Roger Hudspith, the Blues Brothers lead singer and manager, who used the term 'shoot the moon' to mean to leave, split the scene, came up with the idea of moving into a flat in the summer of '67. Although I'd not been thinking about moving out of home, it suddenly seemed like a reasonable idea. I was about ready to move, so I cleared it with my parents, dealt with the predictable questioning, and went to see the place Roger had found in a dull suburb called Purley Oaks, when he dropped the bombshell that his dad would not allow him to move out. I was taken aback by this because it had never occurred to me that Roger was probably still only seventeen at this time, and his father thought he was in charge of whether Roger moved out or not. What perplexed me was that Roger had found the flat, made all the arrangements and asked me to join him, and he hadn't even asked his dad. It made me wonder if there were problems at home.

I decided to go through with it. Typically, instead of losing face and telling my parents it was off after all, I went in search of another flatmate. This did not take long. I ran into John Hobbs, my 'love rival' for Rosalyn from the previous year. We had a 'swift half' in a local pub, and he agreed to move in. I had sort of admired John as a nascent Beat; he seemed pretty cool. So I moved in, and John slept there for one night. Then for a week I stayed there alone, kind of wondering what John was up to. The house was dark and full of young boys renting rooms, with a landlord of a very obvious sexual persuasion. Jimi Hendrix's first album, *Are You Experienced*, was in constant rotation on my Dansette. After that week I called John's house to see what was happening, and John's dad answered the phone.

Upon my enquiring as to the whereabouts of my new flatmate, John's father let me know in no uncertain terms that his son had indeed *not* moved into a flat with me, and that he still lived at home, and this was the first he'd heard of such a thing. He made it sound as if he didn't like the idea much either. Then I considered that John was about seventeen just like Roger, and as cool as he had always seemed, he had in fact told me he was moving in, stayed one night, and gone back home. I was flabbergasted to say the least. My friends had no idea about growing up, getting flats, telling the truth. I decided to shoot the moon and leave Purley Oaks.

I was sacked from the RAC, the job I was still holding onto during this abortive attempt at bedsit living. This was the second job in a row I had been dismissed from, and the second time that I kept the fact from my parents. This time I had been kicking a ball around the office with a couple of the other office lads and knocked over a shelving unit that housed thousands of accounts, this being many years before computer software would take the place of filing. And as I said before, I don't even like football! Chris was sacked a month or two after me.

On 2 July I went up to the Saville Theatre on Shaftesbury Avenue, where we had seen Hendrix again the previous month playing 'Sgt Pepper' in front of Beatles Paul and George. This night I went with Rick, the Blues Brothers guitarist, to see Cream, with Jeff Beck supporting, and Beck blew Cream out of the water for Rick and me. Beck had a reputation reaching all the way back to Croydon groups like the Deltones, even playing at our community centre in New Addington. Prior to the Saville show we had sneaked into the back of the Marquee club, up an alleyway off Wardour Street that you can't get along these days.

We watched John Mayall, who was also to appear at the Saville that night, rehearse his new band. Our enthusiasm for Mayall had gone off the boil by now. It was one thing to have Eric Clapton or Peter Green in the band during the ascension of their powers, but without these guys and at this late hour, the band sounded tired.

Fats Domino and his band had also played the Saville, for six nights in March and April of that year. It was the Fat Man's first-ever trip to the UK. He was supported by Gerry and the Pacemakers, presumably still managed by Epstein, who ran the Saville shows, and the Bee Gees, who suffered the wrath of the Teds, and flying objects, for a week. All four of the Beatles attended the last performance.

On 29 July I went to Alexandra Palace for the 'Love-In', and saw Eric Burdon & the Animals, Pink Floyd, Brian Auger & Julie Driscoll, Arthur Brown, Creation, Tomorrow, Blossom Toes, Sam Gopal's Dream and others. Julie Driscoll totally bowled me over, standing there mid-stage as we walked in, with that big hair and her big deep voice. I thought she was a man at first. She was wonderful, like nothing I'd seen or heard before. I had gone with Rick and his mate Alf Sommerville, our Blues Brothers driver, and some others. Alf kept saying, "Ere, if this is a love-in when's all the love going to 'appen then?' I felt I was never going to be with the cool people.

Inspired by my sacking, and possibly my hopeless football skills, I decided to disband the Blues Brothers and become a 'pro' musician. The Blues Brothers did our last Coal 'Ole gig in July 1967 and I advertised in *Melody Maker* for a working band to join. John MacLean was another of our roadies for the Blues Brothers and he continued to help me out as my driver during that August. Most of the auditions got me nowhere so I helped form a 'folk-blues' group with Pete Lieberman and Will from the Blues Brothers, called Blues Caravan. We did two gigs only, both in September.

As I had kept my July sacking a secret from my parents, I surreptitiously took a casual job on a farm. The farm had been a summer job for Desiree and her school chums, eighteen acres growing nursery produce. I broke up with Desiree while on the farm, and then got the aforementioned lecture from her mother, at a nearby café one lunchtime. There she was waiting for me at the main gate to the farm. Gawd, she was a formidable woman, she made me feel sorry for Desiree. She even had a word with my mum on the phone, who told her where to get off; she had had quite enough of other people's mothers complaining about me. My mother was also more concerned with the fact that, this way, she had discovered her son was working on a farm instead of in the office she thought he was working in.

Can You See Me – Glynnis and Jimi

Glynnis was from Caterham. Glynnis was the ultimate hippy. A florid, friendly girl, with flowing velvet robes, King's Road dresses, big blonde hair. I didn't want to be her boyfriend, but we hung around a lot, went to the same pub, same suburban parties, usually held in nice homes while the parents were away, and sometimes dated to go to a gig. I was between girlfriends. Glynnis was why I ever wore a bell.

By September 1967 I had been wearing a lot of rings for quite some time. It was a style thing. I traded one with Glynnis. She took me to see the Mothers of Invention at the Albert Hall. Despite being a total blues freak, I liked certain bands coming out of the States at that time, like the Mothers and Velvet Underground, as opposed to the West Coast sound that was played everywhere I went, like Jefferson Airplane, who I thought were namby pamby and weak.

We caught the train and travelled uptown to Kensington Gore. She was wearing her usual fabulous homemade robes, out-doing herself. She never seemed to go out with anyone but she was unquestionably hipper than hip. She went to a lot of gigs, too. Saw everyone. That night she was wearing a bell around her neck. Tinkle ding, little bell on a chain. On the train she said, Swap me your ring for my bell. I said okay. I swapped a ring for her silver bell on light silver chain.

I actually wore that bell for a little while after that. It wasn't really *me*, but no-one would laugh at me exactly (except the hard

Surrey Street Market Mods who still hung around the Gun in Old Town Croydon).

At the Albert Hall we had good seats. Glynnis always got good seats. Pretty much centre stage and about twenty or so rows back. The sound was awful at the Albert Hall in those days, whoever you saw. This was the night that Frank Zappa famously suggested Don Preston, keyboard player, go back up in the organ box and play 'Louie Louie' on the 'majestic Albert Hall organ', and the rest of the Mothers would join in to back some guy from the audience who was attempting to play trumpet with them. It was a way of sending the interloper up. It was a cacophony. But cool. They ripped dolls apart that evening as well.

Anyway, before the show started we sat there watching people come in and take their seats, while some got up and walked around. There was a 'choir' section of seats behind the stage, and suddenly from the left-hand side of this area emerged Jimi Hendrix in a new red velvet suit. I say new, because we hadn't seen him in it before and what else would it have been but new on this night? It had a nip-waisted jacket and very tight pants, slightly flared, over Cuban-heeled boots. He had that lanky, stooped way of strolling, hands in pockets. Sort of a shyness mixed with the overbearing desire to show himself (and his suit) off. He sauntered across the corner of the stage to go see someone in the front row, which seemed outrageous – it was not *his* stage. He was at once a mixture of arrogance and *so what*, no one will stop me. Glynnis and I looked over at this sudden red figure walking over the Albert Hall stage, and said nothing about it. It may possibly have been the perfect moment of 1967 for me.

Or it may not.

Chelsea Morning

In September I got a reply from that first *Melody Maker* ad, from a group named the Block. They had done two gigs at the Roundhouse under the name 5 Day Week with Pink Floyd and Soft Machine. They had played what was virtually a residency at Tiles, so they told me, but under what name I don't know, although the following story throws some light on that. They always said that they had named themselves the Block while being asked by the Drug Squad what they were called during a raid on Tiles. This suggests that they had no name on the billing *that* night. Again they may have played a lot of gigs as 'Support Group'.

By late summer 1967 Tiles was a club for latter-day Mods – more like soul boys (and girls); please refer to my 'moddy boys and girls' descriptions in previous chapters. London clubs had been moving on to psychedelia over the past year. The Flamingo had changed hands and was now the Pink Flamingo, a sorry state of affairs. The hip psychedelic club was UFO, on Tottenham Court Road, and it was a shame that a club of such great history as the 'Mingo had stooped so low as to cash in, without gaining credibility. Tiles held 'Soul Nites', radio promotional tie-ins, and the crowds outside always looked like kids from out of town. The Tiles drug of choice was speed – the term 'block' still in use – while at UFO the clientele was tripping out. Tiles mainstay DJ Jeff Dexter, an impossibly boyish-looking bespectacled hippy, with long blond flaxen hair, had mixed psychedelic records in with R&B and ska at his 'Record and Light Show' nights. Now he had moved on to Middle Earth in Covent Garden, which opened for business in August and took over from UFO when that club closed its doors. Jeff, as a young Mod and teenage dancer, had also been the DJ at the Purley Orchid in its heyday, nurtured by his friend Ian Sammy Samwell, hit songwriter of 'Move It', while he was a member of Cliff Richard's Drifters, and 'Whatcha Gonna Do About It' for the Small Faces. Sammy was the rightful claimant to the title of first live disc jockey to work at a dance hall during the ongoing era of live dance bands playing the latest hits. In other words, the first DJ as we now know the term, and a man who introduced R&B records into his dances. Where we might have heard 'Duke of Earl' by Gene Chandler or a new Fats Domino on the Beeb, Sammy was spinning 'Good Morning Little Schoolgirl' by Don & Bob or 'What's Your Name' by Don & Juan, and very early Tamla Motown sides like 'Shop Around', introducing a generation to black American wax a few years before pirate radio would continue the work. Tiles finished up in September.

My fellow members in the Block were singer Dave, bass player Ray and guitarist Alan (not to be confused, if you can manage it, with any other Alan in these pages). Ray and Alan lived at 102 Edith Grove, Chelsea – the Rolling Stones' old flat. This was the address where Brian, Keith and Mick famously lived when their band first formed, in a state of creativity and squalor. When I moved in with the Block, which was out of necessity so that I could get to the gigs, the squalor still remained. Although there had been a three-year gap, they were very aware of the Stones' history there (I think possibly their agent Commercial Entertainments had *something* to do with their getting the flat). The next-door neighbour also remembered the Stones. Sometimes Ray or Alan would forget the front door key, and if the man next door was out, his daughters would be enlisted to let one of the boys in to their house and up to the first-floor balcony, where they could climb over and into the flat at 102. If the father was at home there would be no way. We used to rehearse in the flat during the daytime, and after a while he started banging on the wall and complaining, and at least at one point, said words to the effect of, 'I had this trouble with the Rolling Stones, I'm not having it with you!' This made the Block's day.

The group had started out in their home town of Welwyn Garden City, and Dave still lived there (with his mum, I suppose). Most of the gigs were up in Hertfordshire and Cambridgeshire and we would pick him up on the way. Otherwise, he would travel to the flat in London. A hometown friend of theirs was Mick Taylor, the current guitarist with John Mayall, and Danny, their previous drummer, had been in early bands with him. They talked about the Gods, Taylor's previous group, a lot. Taylor had made it further in music than anyone they (or I) knew. It was a further irony that he would one day become a Rolling Stone.

I moved into 102 Edith Grove, and took my Dansette with me. My record player had been a Christmas gift from Mum and Dad in 1960, had moved with me to the lonely bedsit earlier in the year, and had familiarised itself with lots of music, from Elvis through jazz 78s and on to Hendrix. Mum drove me with all my gear up to World's End, Chelsea, and at the pedestrian crossing opposite Granny Takes a Trip – top boutique to the burgeoning underground scene, and patronised by the Beatles on down – she nearly ran over Eric Clapton. He bowed to her, and I told her who he was. Later I discovered that he hung out at Granny's all the time, as we all did: guys in incredibly bright flowered shirts and orange trousers, girls in long dresses who wore talcum powder on their faces for the extra pallor it afforded. The Block, who were suburban boys dressed up, called it the Cross-Eyed Indian Shop after the décor on the shopfront at that time.

Commercial Entertainments was run by Tony Cousins, a tubby, oily character, with his partner, Bruce White, from an office at 4 Denmark Street. I remember that the Move fan club had an office on the first floor, while Commercial Entertainments was at the top. Galaxy Entertainments was along at number 7, and one of their clients was the Move. Galaxy was the name of the notorious Don Arden's business, and Cousins and White were running something along similar lines it seems. Galaxy Entertainments had a bedsit above their offices. It was rented to a young DJ who worked on the club circuit around the UK. When he travelled away the bedsit was used to 'audition' young female singers. Just outside the door leading to the bedsit was the office kitchen area and on one of the walls hung what looked like a first aid cupboard. But, instead of medical supplies, inside was a two-way mirror where people could view any 'auditions' taking place. So the legends go.

All these music biz offices in Denmark Street were 'manned' by young *ingénues* who lived in flats in Notting Hill along with the majority of the musicians signed to these agents. Sometimes we would go up to the office at number 4 to beg Tony Cousins for money, as we *never* got paid for any gigs, *ever*. I guess Cousins paid the rent on the flat. The boys had signed to Commercial Entertainments before I arrived on the scene, and I never asked how they came to do such a stupid thing. I joined because I was looking to be in a professional group playing paying gigs. Little did I know.

He would dish out incredibly small sums of money, like ten bob each. With this we would buy Wimpy burgers, and back at King's Road we would buy brightly patterned ladies' scarves. Not in the trendy boutiques, but Woolworth's on King's Road. These scarves would serve as clothing items we could give to the local teeny bopper girls who waited outside our gigs, who, for some reason, always requested an item of clothing. Weird, but something to do with the mindset of the time. Okay, you're *nobody* we've heard of, but you're a pop group. Item of clothing, please.

So with a burger in the stomach (I had never *heard* of acid reflux then) and a new scarf at the throat we would drive off to somewhere like Cambridge, where we would play a gig at the Corn Exchange. The number of gigs we played at places with names that ended in Corn Exchange show the level we were on, while at the same time, these unassuming venues up and down the country formed into the bedrock of rock tours for some years to come.

During my tenure of roughly two months, incredibly we *never* actually played as the Block. We played a gig at the Hertford Corn Exchange where we were billed as the Healers. Now, the Healers were a real group, it's just that they were playing a gig somewhere else. Commercial Entertainments had the habit of booking the same band on two different gigs on the same night. To make matters weirder, the Healers were a large all-black band! They were even *billed* as a 'fantastic colored [sic] band'!

Actually, the Healers' drummer was the only white member. His name was Dino Coccia, and I would get to know Dino later in life. Also on that bill in Hertford was Adrian Love, son of bandleader Geoff Love, and a broadcasting DJ making a name for himself cashing in on the flower power scene.

On another gig we replaced Geno Washington and the Ram Jam Band, which was a whole different story. You couldn't fool a couple of hundred Skinheads from somewhere out in the sticks who had paid to see their hero. Skinheads had first made their presence known in 1967. Essentially, these were young men who came in to the Mod movement in its death throes, just as everyone else was becoming a hippy, and froze the last Mod image in time. And then exaggerated it.

Hair shaved close to the head, Brutus versions of Madras shirts, Levi's with one-inch turn-ups, Doc Marten boots. The lady version was similarly frozen in time, with neat skirt suits, clumpy shoes and feathered hair, long at the sides and back. Skinheads loved reggae, were reggae fans *years* before Jamaican music made the big crossover to the rock audience via Bob Marley. The irony was that Skinheads were notoriously racist, while loving black music. Their stance was Englishness, which, taken to its extreme, would end up in xenophobia, and neatness, which gave the Skins their hatred of all hippies, bikers and foreigners. They were the ogre during the 'Summer of Love'.

So here we were standing behind the curtain readying ourselves for three hundred Skinheads, listening to a capacity crowd chanting 'Geno! Geno!' I think they knew, but they weren't about to go home in a town with nothing else to do. The curtains opened on four scarf-wearing hairy white guys playing rock music, albeit including many Tamla and soul stalwarts, too few and too disguised to save our skin, and standing dead still, scared to death, while a *lot* of irate Skins booed. We got away unscathed; the Skins seemed to enjoy venting their anger by chanting before and during our set, but weren't inclined to do anything else but put the fear into us. Meaning they made it uncomfortable for us to play, and we felt stupid going though with it.

Tony and Bruce would arrive in a Ford Thunderbird convertible, usually after we'd started our set. While we were on they operated a light show. It was, after all, 1967, and the liquid light show was obligatory. Somebody must have created their lights for them, as they included among their images slides of naked women. One of our biggest laughs in the van going home to Chelsea would be the memory of a huge breast sliding across the stage, an outrageous incongruity. When this happened we might be playing 'My Girl' or 'The Eagle Flies on Friday' (by the Expectations), way off from the usual psychedelic fare, for punters who wouldn't know what they were meant to be getting from a liquid light show in the first place. All operated by Tony and Bruce. Then before we had finished they had gone. *Always*. I seem to remember we saw the money being handed over by the promoter more than once, or maybe it was what I was told had happened. The one gig the agents did not show up for was the Geno gig! Funny that.

Commercial Entertainments was operating an almost all-black cast of bands, putting them on with a version of a light show more suitable for a rock band, while handling a handful of the top names on the pop circuit at the same time. Another act on Commercial Entertainments' books was the Coloured Raisins, who later changed their name to simply the Raisins. In fact they may have been the biggest act represented exclusively by Tony and Bruce. As the Raisins they had records released in the late sixties, but they changed their name back to the Coloured Raisins at the end of the decade for records on Trojan (the label that Bruce White had joined as A&R man). Lead singer for the Raisins was Earl Green, who was another man I was destined to meet in another lifetime on the gigging scene. By the time Earl had arrived in Britain from Jamaica at thirteen, he had learned his R&B from New Orleans radio stations, and said he 'got the music bug' as a teen at the Flamingo Jazz Club, where 'the air was saturated with steam and music'.

By the time Tony and Bruce were working for Trojan in the seventies, and more British reggae artists had appeared, they got immersed in that scene and formed an agency called Creole, which became a record label. This worked for Desmond Dekker, with great success, and Tony and Bruce become producers in the reggae field.

I left the Block after two or three months, and it was sudden. So sudden I left my precious Dansette in Edith Grove. I did a disappearing act as I couldn't face Ray and the others. I'm not sure I said goodbye. I knew the gigs were thinning out, and I was pretty pissed off with the lack of money. I look back and think that I must have felt those guys were naive and foolish to have got themselves willingly into such a rip-off situation. But I wasn't bold enough to face them and say, 'Look, I only joined you lot out of an *MM* ad and I'm getting no money, what's it all about? I said "pro" in the ad. Why should I join the line waiting for Tony Cousins' hand-outs, do you think I'm a fool too?' I said nothing, because I was too passive, and had followed them wide-eyed. It was easier for me to just stop going to Chelsea. They never got in touch. They knew, didn't they? For the rest of my life I thought of Tony Cousins and Commercial Entertainments as the real culprits who had buggered up my first shot at 'going pro'. It was no fault of Ray, Alan and Dave.

Tony Cousins remained a business partner in Creole with Bruce White all along, and was shot dead while on a trip to Jamaica in 2003, where he had always taken care of the sharp end of the firm. Bruce White sold the company's recorded works to Sanctuary Records Group that year. He died of cancer late in 2011.

Going Home

At the end of 1967, living at home once more, and in response to Mum's question, 'So now what are you going to do about money?' I signed on at the Labour Exchange. Before long I was back frequenting the Royal Oak in Surrey Street. It was here, the first day of my return, that I ran into Rosalyn, the 'Julie Christie' figure who had driven me to jealousy the previous year with her line of boyfriends. She was also making her first appearance here since returning from some Continental wandering. She had spent the summer living with Smiler, one of the Beats we had admired so much in the recent past. Upon her return from travelling, things, as they say, were different. I immediately had the feeling that Rosalyn was now 'doing monogamy'. This was the start of my first serious love affair since Kathy, back in the teen years of 1964.

* * *

That November we saw Cream at Silver Blades Ice Rink in Streatham SW16, Rosalyn now being my gigging companion. I genuinely lost count of the times I saw this group between 1966 and 1968. It's weird, looking back, as the drummer and bass player, Jack 'n' Ginger, were both more than a little despicable, with their snotty pretensions towards jazz, which neither of them had really made a mark in, anyway. I didn't particularly dig either of them as players. I think most Cream fans made no bones about the fact that they came to Cream gigs because of Eric Clapton.

By this point the whole Cream show was beginning to bore me, however, and had, in fact, not too long to run.

Silver Blades was just one of a collection of entertainment centres in Streatham that made that suburb a hip destination, something just short of *real* London. For gigs at the ice rink, wooden flooring was put over the ice, and most of the top rock names on the circuit appeared there. Chris tells me he came and saw me play there once – it must have been some early amateur gig of some sort that I have no memory of at all.

There was also a huge bowling alley in Streatham called the Streatham Bowl. This had been Mod central, with kids being picked from there to dance on *Ready Steady Go!* back in its mid-sixties heyday, and 'Queen of the Mods' Cathy McGowan being a resident of the area. Then there was SW16's palais, the Streatham Locarno, on a par with the grandeur of the Purley Orchid and the Wimbledon and Hammersmith Palais. Nestling just behind St Leonard's Church was the Swing Shop, south London's answer to Dobell's, the jazz and folk specialist on Charing Cross Road where all we blues freaks bought our hard-to-find LPs. There was also a café in Streatham that had a Scopitone Jukebox, that is to say one of those rare machines that showed little films that promoted some records. I remember seeing a film of Screaming Lord Sutch doing 'Jack the Ripper' there in around 1964. I think we kidded ourselves the film was as scary as Sutch's act was reputed to be. When I did eventually see His Lordship late in '66, he lived up to his reputation, prancing around the stage, setting light to it, berating the audience, screaming his lungs out, doing everything except really singing, which he couldn't do. His band, the Savages, were fantastic.

The southern end of Streatham is the beginning of Norbury. Also the end of London postcodes, as Streatham has a London postcode but Norbury does not. Norbury is, well, it's sort of Croydon. There used to be a huge pub, the King William IV, at the point on the London Road where SW16 ends. As London pubs closed at eleven o'clock during the week and outside London they closed at ten thirty, this meant that this was the first pub travelling north along the London Road that closed at eleven during the week. If you were drinking south of this point, as my mates and I would be, you would load into a car and belt over to the William and get in another half hour's drinking. A ritual.

* * *

So I signed on – as a musician, which caused much 'You can't seriously sign on as a musician' kind of chat from the morons behind the desk at the Croydon Labour Exchange – and spent a lot of time hanging out. Rosalyn and I couldn't see enough of each other. Her father owned a soft furnishings shop and on Tuesdays Rosalyn's mother would work in the shop. This meant that every Tuesday, all day Tuesday, we would spend in bed at her house in the upper-middle-class environs of Sanderstead. Her mother never came home for lunch, thankfully.

I put another ad in *Melody Maker* in December, and the only response I got from it netted me a one-off gig on Christmas Eve at the old Addington Hotel. It was an agency job, and the gig was playing in a duo with a piano player. As an acknowledgement of the occasion I kissed more women than I had kissed all year, and spent Christmas with the flu.

Gold

During the auditioning period that led to my next 'pro job' I sat in with a blues band called Skye Wine, who were managed by an attractive and astute young lady called Barbara Deane. She was putting a new band together around a young guitarist, the name of which was going to be Sweet Pain. The guitarist and I sat in for a couple of tunes during a Skye Wine gig. I passed the audition but a week or so later I had to call Barbara to tell her I wasn't going to be in the new group. I had heard from Roger Hudspith, the Blues Brothers singer and my failed flatmate, who had just started working for a band who had gigs waiting and were looking for a drummer.

They were called Gold. I went with Roger's band because of the waiting gigs, as I was still desperate to work as a 'pro' musician. Skye Wine opened for people like Ten Years After and Aynsley Dunbar, and were a similar band to the one I was about to join, while Sweet Pain, the band I turned down, would actually form and go on to pretty much the same level as Gold. Nevertheless, I did have some regrets about the direction I took. Skye Wine, incidentally, once had Jimi Hendrix sit in on bass at the Speakeasy.

During the three or four months after our meeting again at the Royal Oak, Rosalyn and I were both living at home and were desperate to find a flat. We would do the weekend meet-up and 'Where's the party at?' number that was still carrying on at this time. Once or twice, when no party seemed to be happening, we took a train and went up to a small street off Old Brompton

Road in South Kensington, where my friend Maurice lived with a bunch of fellow Chelsea Art School students.

Maurice was someone I had met around the pubs we frequented, the possessor of a shock of curly red hair, and an outspoken and well-informed attitude that made him argumentative but very attractive. We actually went all the way to Maurice's in order to spend the night shagging. One such night we took to Maurice's room, having just arrived, and with his jocular warning not to stain his sheets, we climbed into Maurice's sack. Partly because we woke each other up throughout the night with the young lust that had waited a week, and partly because everyone in the house and their friends seemed to be making so much clatter, we slept very little that night. In the morning, as we left in the quiet before anyone rose, we were surprised to find the entire house had been painted overnight. We silently left a garishly hued hall, the whole house smelling strongly of paint fumes, and slipped out into the Kensington morning.

It was during this time, between late '67 and early '68, that the highly influential film *Bonnie and Clyde* hit the screens. Rosalyn and I got a bit carried away by the 'look', and before long I had asked Dad to dig out an old brown trilby I remembered he had. Matched with my brown leather flying jacket I'd got from the Swap Shop, I figured I had the thirties mobster look down, and Rosalyn took to wearing berets with an imitation black fur coat.

It was also during this time of living with our parents that Rosalyn and I had a 'bun in the oven' scare. My old mate Alan was going steady with a close friend of Rosalyn's, and by an ironic set of circumstances they were now living in a huge old pile of a house that was due for demolition, a house that Rosalyn had shared with Smiler the previous year. Rosalyn went to her friend to ask if there was anything she could do about her predicament. I was sweating bullets. We got invited over for dinner ostensibly for the girls to get the job 'done', and possibly for the more mature

Alan to shake his head at me and purse his lips. At the eleventh hour Rosalyn received proof of not being pregnant after all and we went along anyway, and over dinner celebrated our narrow escape with our friends.

* * *

Gold, the band I had just joined, was a reconstituted blues band made up of a couple of art students called John Chichester and Tony Burroughs. The other member was a surly bass player called John Sheils, who was always leaving because he was on a promise from some pro band or another. I did get to stay at his flat in Holborn frequently so that I could get to and from gigs, as I was still living at home, allowing me to enjoy the environs of 'town' for a while.

A regular gig was Middle Earth, at which the DJ was Jeff Dexter. One found out very quickly that Jeff was the DJ, or promoter, or something at *any* club that was hip. He was omnipresent. Middle Earth was an enormous basement in Covent Garden, entered through a huge set of double doors. Once inside, one was engulfed in a patchouli-drenched atmosphere of flickering lights, swimming sounds, wavering people dancing somewhere in the dark. Jeff would spin some of the longer, more experimental tracks coming out at the time, leading to a regular bunch of 'idiot' dancers being the only ones staying the course. There were two stages. The main band would play the larger stage, and the next on the bill would play the smaller, while bands further down the bill would play the larger stage, but earlier on. It meant that while one band was breaking down its gear, another band could already be set up on the stage opposite.

The early mornings after Middle Earth were a blurry stroll through the market among fruit and veg buyers and sellers and general madness. Goodbye, the real Covent Garden. It was, for me, an echo of the barrows and strewn cauliflowers of Croydon's Surrey Street, but on a grand scale. I played with Gold at Middle Earth on a night when hundreds of Skinheads had arrived in the early hours with the intention of causing disturbance and busting heads. The doors were locked and the police were called. The police, who had their own interests in the club, took a very long time to arrive, lending to the occasion the feeling of a siege. At least their delay gave those carrying drugs enough time to dispense with them. We played our set during the 'seige', and for me it was déjà vu, feeling like the night with the Block, only on a grander scale. When the police arrived, they used the occasion as an excuse to search pockets and velvet shoulder bags, as the Skins had dispersed.

We also played the Whiskey A Go-Go and the Scotch of St James. Gold were really my last go-round at being professional for a while. The gigs we played put me on the same stage as Zoot Money, the Yardbirds and John Mayall (with Mick Taylor).

In March 1968 Rosalyn and I moved into my friend George the Painter's flat on Lower Addiscombe Road. George was a non-college-educated artist whose shoulder-length Brian Jones hair was the attraction for a whole year of female students at Croydon Art School. He had asked if I wanted to move in with him to help pay the rent and take up the space of a large one-bedroomed flat, and I had told him I wanted to move in with my girlfriend. George was reluctant, but allowed it. We lasted two months with George and then in May moved to Heathfield Road, South Croydon, to be on our own. It was a Morgan Rowland property – Morgan Rowland was a letting agent based at West Croydon that supplied a huge number of flats to young people in the area, and whose properties all seemed to feature the same black-and-white lino.

In March Gold had had their van stolen, causing a short break in the gigs. We went back to gigging and at the end of that month did one at Camberwell School of Art, where, because of the lack of transport, I had to leave my bass drum. It got stolen.

In April I started working as a cutter for a tent-maker's firm way up the Brighton Road near Cane Hill in Surrey. Cane Hill was a mental hospital before government cuts made such establishments a thing of history. It took until May before the drum was recovered, just as Rosalyn and I were moving from George's to South Croydon, and in June I appeared in court as the plaintiff and got the drum back. At this point I had lost much of the enthusiasm for 'turning pro', and without that desire, I found myself not playing at all, for quite a long time.

So, by the spring of 1968 Rosalyn and I had moved into a one-bedroomed flat on the middle floor at the back of a house in South Croydon. The house was at the end of the terrace on a corner. Opposite, where the houses on the other side of the road ended, was the entrance to a cemetery. My final fling of the sixties at going pro had ended ignominiously; I had taken a job and settled into co-habiting bliss with Rosalyn. We made a go of it, thinking this was what we wanted. June and July passed by. I didn't see much of any of our friends for a while. As for Rosalyn and me, it just never seemed to be smooth. I was always antsy. Once we had moved into Heathfield Road, we always seemed to be arguing.

Rosalyn's mother had come round to see me once when Rosalyn was not there. Said that she and Rosalyn's father disapproved of the way she was living. Took her a while! She told me that Rosalyn was due to come into an inheritance when she was twenty-one (she had just turned twenty), and that if she was still living in sin with me, she would see to it that she did not inherit. I thought, I used to know this woman, she liked me. What happened? She must have been kept in the dark about the co-habiting until now. Anyway, she was angry, upset and pissed off. This was the sixties, Mr Jones!

In August, Rosalyn and I ferried over to Calais to meet Mum

and Fred and drive to Dortmund. All four of us drove together across France and through Germany, and I was taken aback at how 'chummy' Mum and Fred were. More had been going on in the last four years or so than I had imagined. I had been so in the dark about their relationship. We had had no communication at all. But I was choked into silence by their obvious feeling they could be this open about it in front of me. I was less than amused at my mother's chirpy demeanour, which did not last throughout the rest of the holiday without Fred.

The day after we got back to England, Mum came round to our flat and asked to speak to me in private. Downstairs in her car she told me that Dad and she were 'no more'. Actually she said, '405 is no more', alluding to the house number where I had spent my life with my parents. So, Mum had got home from Germany to a huge row, I supposed, and at the end of it, Dad had told her that was it.

She had elected to be the one to move out, or at least that's what she said. She had moved in with Fred, and told me she had no choice, but would have preferred not to. After taking her time settling into the idea of living with Fred, they would eventually marry, which is why Mum went through the divorce I mentioned.

That trip to Germany was a distraction from the ups and downs of co-habiting life for me and Rosalyn. When we were back, in order to smooth things over, Rosalyn came up with the idea of going to Spain with a friend of hers for a little holiday. Sweet girl, she just wanted to make it work. We'd just got back from a holiday, her mum was giving her hell, on the verge of disowning her, my folks had split up, and she was volunteering to go off again, to give our relationship a chance. Sure, I said, and off she went.

She hitched across Europe with a girlfriend, and they made it all the way down to Torremolinos. Now, in 1968 Torremolinos was already a tourist attraction and a destination for office girls and Frank Sinatra alike. I imagined horse-drawn carts, skyscrapers and discothèques vying for position; I wouldn't know. Rosalyn was a romantic, read whole French novels in French without understanding that much of what was going on in them, and mused over the black mountains on the trip down to Torremolinos. And got suntanned.

Me, I did not go crazy. I went to work. Some friends, including old girlfriends, came round to see me. Not much happening. I lived a quiet life, working, still drinking at the Royal Oak, sometimes taking up an offer to ride down to Brighton and spend the night under the pier. Yes, this was still a major option in the late sixties, a tradition among Beats, Mods and Rockers alike, and nowadays disallowed. 'Dance to the Music' by Sly Stone always brings those nights to mind. The soundtrack to the last days of sleeping on Brighton beach was played out by acoustic guitars, tin drums and flat voices. The faces of my companions on these trips have faded with the urgent debate that they instigated. I was feeling a two-way pull between the way I was living and the salty Brighton air.

Then I met Lee.

An American Friend

One evening after I had been working at the tent-making company, some mates knocked at the front door, kind of late. It was a lad called Alf who had been connected with the Blues Brothers as a driver, Rick from the Blues Brothers and what can best be described as a full-on freak. Lee was all that a hippy should be. My mates looked sheepishly at me. They had met Lee somewhere in town, at a club, and they had offered him a place to stay. My place. These were guys who lived at home, right? I don't think we had a phone. Imagine a world with no mobiles, no immediate communication. This was it. Lee needs somewhere to stay, right?

Lee was from Berkeley, California. You pronounce that Berkeley, as in hurt, not like the clerk in the bank. One had so much to learn. Lee had long hair past his shoulders, straggly but clean. His clothes are lost to me in time, together with his second name. When he said he was from Berkeley he meant he had been to çollege there. Where he was originally from I have no idea. Lee moved in, and onto my living room floor. That first evening we talked late into the night, two strangers, but I was impressed and relaxed in his company. He had a lot to say.

On the following night Lee brought back a chick. A bit cheeky really, but he was polite about it. This was the sixties, after all. Give me some time, a couple of years, and I would tell them to sling their hook.

Lee and this chick were talking to each other in my flat,

and I was really not included. She was wearing (amazing that I remember this) a tight shocking pink shiny dress that had as many holes in it as material. Lots of flesh showing. She was acting 'out of it' (I was sure even then it was an act), and she had a foreign accent. She was talking about how many drugs she'd taken on what occasions. Much of what she seemed to have ingested was vast amounts of LSD (!) followed by copious quantities of Mandrax. Two drugs I had no experience of at the time, although I suspected, and was eventually proved correct, that neither drug would or could be consumed in the quantities she was boasting of. And, as I said, *they* were talking to each other, but actually she was talking to Lee. I figured at the time that he may have wanted to get her into bed, but actually I think she latched on to him and he just couldn't get rid of her. What was this swinging type chick doing with this out-and-out freak type, when she was also way under his IQ level? I was perhaps being a bit cruel.

One night very soon after this, Lee came back with some other people. They crashed on the living room floor. I went to my bedroom along the landing, and this was the night that Rosalyn came back late from Spain and her travels. Who did these bodies belong to all over the floor? Yeah, well, now it's time to have a word with Lee. But first, it was the middle of the night, and Rosalyn was climbing into bed. I couldn't see her tan, but I could feel it. Smooth, silky, warm. She was uptight, trying to come to terms with me allowing the flat to become a crash pad, she had trodden on someone in the dark. I was horny, and wanting to console. Once she'd relaxed the homecoming was better than ever, but was not destined to last. However, from then on it was Lee on his own, and he stayed for quite a while: him, Rosalyn and me.

Pretty quickly Lee figured me for a guy he wanted to hang with rather than just the owner of a crash pad. He and I would spend a lot of time nattering. I would spin LPs, and he would tell me about, for instance, Wolfman Jack. Now, I had never heard of Wolfman

Jack. Not too many Brits had at that time. This was 1968, and the Wolfman was at that time broadcasting out of Tijuana, Mexico, and being transmitted all the way up the coast of California. In fact, these were the very years his reputation was forged with the new underground rock audience. Lee spun me the whole yarn, the powerful signal coming from South of the Border, 'illegal actually, you know'. Lee was very into the blues, and it seems the Wolfman was broadcasting a lot of blues at that time.

The San Francisco and Berkeley scene had its own brand of rock music, usually lumped together now as Acid Rock, and it had hit London pretty big. In fact, the most important DJ playing it was Jeff Dexter, but I was no longer seeing or hearing anything of him since Middle Earth. So far, being a total blues fanatic, I had avoided all this West Coast stuff like the plague. So Lee, relating to the blues side, told me about seeing all the 'kings' at one gig: B.B., Albert and Freddy. That's the kind of thing that they put on in those days in 'Frisco. And the Wolfman used to spin early Elvis.

So Lee and I had Elvis in common, and I would play him some slightly later Elvis, like 'A Mess of Blues', and he would say, 'Hey that's pretty funky.' This was a new word to me. He tried hard to turn me on to some of the 'Frisco bands, like Big Brother and the Holding Company, who I almost liked for five minutes. I played a record by Tommy James and the Shondells one day, and Lee said, 'Oh, Tommy James, he's a fascist.'

I was getting exposed, through Lee, to this complete culture happening thousands of miles away, where certain West Coast bands were holding sway, where a mythical character called Wolfman Jack was pumping blues and rock 'n' roll into the air from down Mexico way, where kids like 'us' mixed our political views with our music at the drop of a hat. Lee would tell me about a couple of white blues artists that he thought were tough. One was John Hammond and the other was Charlie Musselwhite. He was especially into Musselwhite. I had seen Charlie's name down among the credits on a Chicago blues LP, but knew nothing about him. Lee told me he was a greaser type: hair slicked back, had used to hang with Elvis in Memphis, and was an alcoholic.

One afternoon, because Lee was hungry, we tripped over to what was either a Wimpy Bar in West Croydon or a second-class imitation of one (something like a Golden Egg or a Hungry i). I took Lee in there, and he ordered a burger. When it arrived he asked the waitress what it was. She told him it was a burger. He politely responded that she had made a mistake and that it was not a burger. You probably get where this was going. After we laughed about the burger, Lee explained about how in the States burgers came with a quarter pound of minced steak within the bun. They were called quarter pounders and things like that. Oh, England.

We went there to eat often. We would order eggs. A fry-up more or less. Our breakfast would arrive and then Lee would bend down towards his plate, with his face very close to the food. When I first saw this I wondered what the hell he was up to. Then there was a sucking noise and Lee had sucked up the yolk from his fried egg in one straight suck. When he leaned back in his seat, the fried egg had a hole in the skin over the yolk about the size of a pin prick. I was quite bemused by this, not to mention nauseated.

There was one other thing Lee talked about a lot. Now, I had run with the scene that had protested the Vietnam war in London, and was anti-Vietnam war and anti U.S. foreign policy like many of my generation. But Lee was an American and he was nineteen. He explained that he had three choices. When he got back home his college days were finished. That meant that he could get called up. He did not the fuck want to go to Vietnam. If he became a conscientious objector he would do prison time. He did not the fuck want to spend any time in a Californian penitentiary. His third, and only other choice was to stay out of the country. This would mean living somewhere illegally, losing his passport, and maybe totally relinquishing his citizenship. Never seeing his family again. No choice at all.

Lee had not made up his mind by the time he left. When he got back home he sent me a package with two LPs in it – John Hammond and Charlie Musselwhite – and a letter, just as he said he would do. I wrote back to him, but then the trail went cold. I never knew what happened to Lee, the first American I ever got close to, the one who told me a lot of what I needed to know. It took me a long time to stop thinking about Lee. He had left an indelible mark. He was funny, he was kind, he was witty, and above all . . . he was cool. I guess it would help if I could remember his second name.

Lee was also the first American of his generation, and I eventually would know a few, who actually talked to me about that dilemma that I know shaped the lives of so many, and fucked up the futures of a few too many, too. He was a young man from a country that was sending its young men abroad to die . . . or worse.

Next time I heard of Wolfman Jack was with the 1973 movie, *American Graffiti*, the film that blew Wolfman's cover and changed everything for him, as the film spread the legend around the world. The first time I personally heard Wolfman on the air was in 1978, on my first trip to Los Angeles. I thought of Lee ten years before. And the Wolfman was still playing the blues.

Leaving Here

In May 1968 there had been violent student riots in Paris, causing mayhem and destruction and the re-instatement of French war hero Charles de Gaulle as President. The Situationists' ideas were still influencing much happening in France, and the happenings in France were influencing much elsewhere. These riots, and similar events in Chicago in April, marked the end of the peace and love movement of the Summer of Love the previous year. In March and October of 1968 there were large and violent demonstrations in London against the Vietnam war. I attended the October one, along with some of my friends, Maurice among them. Much of the day was spent dodging the most extreme pockets of violence, like people being trampled under horses. Bloodied faces rushing past me were a reminder of the complacent life I already led at age twenty with my pressing concerns about rented flats and relationships. A bunch of us discussed the day's excitement at the Gun Tavern.

In September Chris married Holly, and Rosalyn and I were wedding guests. In October the American Folk Blues Festival came to Fairfield Hall and I saw Jimmy Reed, John Lee Hooker, Walter Horton, Eddie Taylor, T-Bone Walker, Curtis Jones and Big Joe Williams. I think I went with Rick from the Blues Brothers, among others.

Rosalyn and I were drifting apart. That is, I was drifting away from the idea of settling down in a relationship. After all the fight with her parents, it seemed ironic, the previous estrangement from her parents futile. But we were twenty, and while she may have been ready for this, I was feeling moves inside me, other ways to go and other places to see. Rosalyn had the idea of moving into a house with four nurses in south London somewhere. It was poignant and a little sad when I went over there and stayed occasionally, as we were still officially going out, but not living together. It seemed a step back for her to be sharing with a bunch of other single girls, and I felt awkward around her housemates.

Rosalyn moved out. Chris Reeves moved in. I had met the other important Chris in my life nearly two years before. It was at the Star, on a Monday folk night. Our mutual love of *Mad* magazine, a good-fitting trouser and rambunctious pop music were some of the jumping-off points that led to our trading clobber, forming endless groups, and laughing about the state of the world. In fact, I had been round to Chris's parents' place a couple of times with the express purpose of trading clothes with him. I got a marvellous frock coat in pinstripe grey. It seems to have been a thing that Chris and his friends had done during their Mod days, swapping gear. Add to that he had been attempting to break into the pop world during the same timeframe as me. He'd had a couple of groups with the wonderful names the Dyaks and Psycho's Daisies.

He kept it to himself at the time but he had an insufferable home life, and he and I shared a humour we could rely on to help us forget life's daily drudge. That winter was cold, and we had not the means to heat the two rooms, separated as they were by the long landing. We closed the bedroom down and moved the double mattress into the living room, turning it into a studio flat, as the kitchenette was over by the window in the same room. The walls started to sport some of our favourite expressions writ large across them, thanks to Chris. The mice, damn them, spent the nights noisily strolling across the cold fat in the bottom of the frying pan.

At the beginning of January I turned twenty-one. Mum, who

had been living with Fred for four or five months, held a birthday party for me. She booked a function hall behind the Gun Tavern. This pub had been, and would continue to be for some time, a local music venue. We saw a lot of good jazz there, mainly on boozy Sunday lunchtimes. That would be my first period of enjoying the benefits of beer mixed with jazz, and those sessions at the Gun were the place to see all of local life, from the Surrey Street hardcases to the goateed intellectuals, the Woolworth's girls to the girls whose money came from Daddy and were usually dragging a greyhound behind them. There were jug bands, the successors to skiffle groups, playing on folk nights, and the back hall was host to everyone from the Small Faces to our own little jam sessions we sometimes organised.

The birthday party must have cost Mum a fortune, which she was probably struggling for at that time. She asked me to invite my friends and arrange some music. Chris R. had a group called Thor, and they were duly booked. As a sort of support act I got a blues band together that included Blues Brother Rick. Plus, of course, I invited all my friends. Added to this were a good many heads who gatecrashed. A group of students from Croydon School of Art crashed, including some faces who would become friends in the years to come. I have it on good authority that the attraction that night was 'Some older hip people, all friends with this guy, Brian. He's engaged!' So that's the reputation that living with someone and not going out much gets you.

Luckily I turned twenty-one about a year before my serious drug intake really took off. One year later the gatecrashers, and even some close friends, would have upset my mother even more than this lot did. I was getting worried questions concerning young folk who were coming to the bar and asking for another glass of gin or vodka, when they had only just finished their last one. Yes, Mum, if the drinks are free, this is what you'll find.

It must have been the one and only occasion when my entire

family shared space with my shabby and not-so-shabby friends. Dad, who had nothing to do with the financing or organising of the affair, was there, but would be present at fewer and fewer of the important affairs in my life. He said the same thing then as he would say when I got married three years later. 'Let me know how much you want, won't you?'

That party turned out to punctuate my life in a way. Rosalyn had moved out, and I installed my birthday present one-piece stereo gramophone in the flat that I now shared with Chris R. That stereo would see a lot of action in the coming years.

Soon after this, Chris came home to the flat with a girl. I cannot remember her name, but she had been the girlfriend of someone we knew, a bit of a nutter, and they had split up. Chris was not bringing this woman home for any other reason than the fact that I fancied her, and I had mentioned it to him. Weirdo gift. Soon we were joined by two chaps who had started to appear around the flat occasionally since Chris had moved in. One was none other than Johnny Blunt, still a member of the Searchers, and the other a good friend of both of the other guys, from the same estate as John, who was known affectionately as Droopy. It was decided immediately that some charge was needed, that no-one in Croydon seemed to be 'holding', and that the only way anyone could think of to get some was the time-honoured way of cruising up to Brixton and scoring off the street or in one of the pubs along the Atlantic Road. A dodgy business, but a risk you had to take if charge was what you wanted.

Now, all three guys left to go and score, where only two would or should have gone, in John's Mini. All three went because Chris wanted to honour the fact he'd brought this girl home, by allowing me to be alone with her. Now, whateverhernamewas and I spent the evening talking and snogging, and it must have been late already, because without any discussion we hit the sack. What followed was a half hour or so of embarrassment as

I wasted Chris's present by failing in the manly art of seduction. The girl didn't mind, and we carried on talking, God knows about what. As it got later we started thinking something was wrong. The guys were definitely supposed to be coming back – where else would they go? Would they decide that I wanted to be alone with whateverhernamewas? Eventually we slept, and waking in the morning we knew, knew for sure, something was wrong.

I don't remember how and when I found out, because Chris never came home. The three of them got busted. Three white guys in a Mini down the Atlantic Road late in the evening in the late sixties. Risky? It was crazy. As far as the police were concerned, there was only one reason for a white boy to be cruising around there at that time. Chris and Droopy were under twenty-one, and got remanded in custody at Ashford in Kent, with a free drastic haircut. John was twenty-one and got remanded too, but at Brixton. The law was very tough on even first-time drug offenders. Poor old Johnny had to call the Searchers' road manager and tell him he couldn't make a few gigs. After his case, Chris found himself at the mercy of his merciless father and a prisoner in his own home. So what was new?

That left me alone in my flat once more. I never saw whateverhernamewas again, and I had other pressing issues on my mind. Rosalyn and I, still together but living apart, went to see the Nice one night, an early example of a prog rock group, at Beckenham. They were appearing at a place called the Mistrale Club, right by Beckenham Junction station. It was a bit of a ska and reggae hang-out, in other words catering more to Skinheads, but had groups on too, over two floors. Now, the Nice were not a band I'd particularly been into, and spare me the extravagances of their leader's later ensemble, the name of which I shall not grace these pages with. (For those too young to know, or too ashamed to admit they know, let me say that the leader was Keith Emerson and his later trio were known worldwide as a prog outfit of quite some ostentation.)

At this gig the Nice were performing as a trio, and I have to say, I found it very entertaining, always having found a rocking Hammond to my liking, ever since Georgie Fame and the Blue Flames. At the end of the night we walked back to the flat in South Croydon, a distance of about six miles, which astounds me when I think of it now; we certainly did some Shanks's back then. We had a kind of semi-argument all the way back, and by the time we reached Heathfield Road I had told Rosalyn that I wanted to split up. That is, really split up, not just live apart. I had not gone out with the intention of bringing the evening to a head like that, but somehow my inner thoughts outed themselves. When we climbed into bed we were splitting up, and I felt sad, while she kept asking questions concerning the parameters of the separation. I would think there's a place in her heart where she will never forgive me for for what I did next.

As if I hadn't done enough harm already, I wanted to make a break from Rosalyn; it was painful for it to drag on like this. I saw George the Painter, at whose flat on Lower Addiscombe Road Rosalyn and I had lived for a couple of months, and where he still lived on his own. I asked him if he wanted me back, *sans* girlfriend, and he said, yeah. I called Dad, asked him to help move me with his car, like quick, now. As I also owed Morgan Rowland a bit of rent, I did a moonlight, as they used to say. In more ways than one. And Dad helped me.

After I was ensconced in George's flat, settling in, I got a call from Dad. The phone was down a flight of stairs in the hall. Rosalyn had called him, worried, she had no-one else to ask. He promised her he'd talk to me. He couldn't believe I'd done this disappearing trick without telling her. He was a brick in some ways, really. I called her back. After this she visited me a few times in the early days of Addiscombe, but not for long. Rosalyn and I remained in touch by letters for some time, but soon disappeared from each other's lives.

Whenever I hear 'Courting Blues' by Bert Jansch I think of Rosalyn.

Addiscombe was the beginning of a wild and woolly phase.

Wham Bam Thank You Ma'am

The year 1969 was one of intense drug experimentation for all who hung out at Lower Addiscombe Road. It reached a point where the experimentation overtook the common sense. We had a craze for drinking Demerol, an opiate that was freely available across the counter at the time. By that I mean specifically at the chemist across the road. We would divide one bottle between two. Then a bunch of us would, say, go and see *Fantasia* at the cinema. Crazy.

In the spring, after I had shared the flat with George and his paintings quietly enough, Chris R., who had had enough with living with his miserable old man, moved in and slept on the floor of the bedroom. We continued our friendship that had been cemented during the cold winter in the previous flat, and came to an agreement where I did the cooking in exchange for Chris's skills at a layered haircut.

After some time a character called Alan Male seemed to just appear. He was introduced to us by Chris. He didn't know either George or me, but moved in and spent many sleepless weeks in an old armchair, drawing in a sketchpad. He had no need of a bed as he kept himself awake with French blues, the popular amphetamine tablets from the club scene. Alan was an ex-Mod, which is how he knew Chris. Although, I believe it had been Droopy who had brought him round and left him with us. He had the most infectious smile I have ever known, he would smile readily at anyone and anything. He had a very happy disposition.

And, as many remarked at the time, he seemed to dance rather than merely walk.

Alan had just stopped hanging out with a bunch of guys who were still clinging onto the old Mod scene, like elder statesmen. They were our age, of course, but looked like middle-aged Skinheads. Two or three of them would gather on the other side of the road opposite our building, looking up at our first-floor bay window. When Alan made rare forays into the outside world they would accost him and ask why he was living with those 'ippies. Except they used the term, ''ip geezers', which was something of a compliment by my terms.

Alan's French blues were a revelation as I had not done any uppers at that point. He sold them to anybody who wanted them, and they came in handy for our weekend forays up to 'Midnight Court' at the Lyceum Ballroom, where that year we saw Marsha Hunt, the Pretty Things, the Bonzo Dogs, Steppenwolf and quite a few more besides. The point about 'Midnight Court' was that it was all night, hence the blues coming in useful. A bunch of us would arrive back at Addiscombe on the Saturday morning and hang around the flat for a few hours, coming down. The problem with uppers is that you have to come down before you can sleep. We would skin up a few joints to smooth over the worst of it. At some point one needed the loo in an awful hurry; why the pills did this I have no idea, but there would be a queue for the bathroom, with all of us laughing like maniacs. Some people did downers to ease the comedown. Very popular back in those days were Mandrax, a hypnotic. The thing to do with Mandies would be to take one, and then fight the sleep they could induce. You were left with a lovely, fuzzy, drunk kind of stupor, and a bold libidinous feeling. Hence they acquired the nickname, 'Randy Mandies'. It must be said, however, that no matter how randy or friendly Mandies made you feel, they made you look really stupid. Nevertheless, I liked them, and once decided to drop a couple of

Mandies instead of the 'doobs' for our 'Midnight Court' session. I slept right in front of Led Zeppelin, all the way through their set!

This was a very good year generally for gigs. There were the free concerts in Hyde Park, including the Stones in June, of course. We also saw some good gigs at Fairfield Hall, including a blinder from the Who, which I attended with Chris R. It was during the time that Alan was our source for the blues that he came up with the phrase, 'No money no drugs,' while his tongue was firmly in his cheek. A cheek belonging to a particularly thin yellowish skin, with wispy hair that he was trying to grow. In fact, that's why he was hanging out and staying in our armchair: he wanted to grow his hair, and not appear in public until it had grown. Well, it never did grow, partly because of the amazing amount of speed that Alan had ingested, or maybe it was just the type of hair that didn't grow. Another expression I remember was his stock answer to anyone who offered him gum, popular among those doing 'doobs': 'I don't chew.'

The group that gathered regularly at Addiscombe grew at an alarming rate. Although in retrospect it seems as if the place was like Victoria Station, most days there was a regular kernel of people there. My one-piece stereo came in for its first bout of serious use. And abuse. I had a treasured copy of Jerry Lee Lewis *Live at the Star Club Hamburg*, an LP hard enough to sit still to at the best of times. On one occasion Chris tried to leap, with uncontrolled exuberance, straight on to the turntable while the LP was doing its work. I couldn't blame him, even as I watched my first of many copies of that superb album die a noble death. We discovered some time after this that George owned a 78 of Gene Vincent's 'Dance to the Bop'. On the deck it went one evening when we were all quite out of it. Chris avoided the record deck, but we destroyed quite a bit of furniture that night. George loved it. And to think all this was in the year of Woodstock.

Chris and I were greatly amused by George's not wearing

underpants. One day we discovered the reason why. There was a closet/airing cupboard in the bedroom that seemingly wasn't being used. We opened the door one day and about six months' worth of dirty laundry tumbled out onto the floor. Among this pile were of course all the underpants George had started out wearing when he had first moved in. He had not included them in the wash he took regularly over to his mum's, and there they were, rotting in the bedroom cupboard. Chris and I tried to shut the door without touching the laundry, but it was impossible. For some time it stayed that way, about a foot ajar with the soiled undies peeking through. One day, as George was definitely not going to do anything about the situation, we decided to get the laundry out of the cupboard and burn it. We waited until we knew George would be out for the night. I was wearing some Marigolds, and Chris was holding some large bags open for me to dump the offending items into. Way in the back of the cupboard was a worn out/washed out pair of jeans that caught my eye.

I said to Chris, 'These jeans have fly buttons.'

'Yeah, they're Levi's button fronts,' he said, 'let's get this shit out of here before George gets back.'

Up to that time I had worn Levi's from Millets, ever since the day, nearly three years earlier, that Chris had advised me to dump my Matelots and get some Levi's, if I knew what was good for me. I had always been disappointed with the shape and character of the English-made zip-front Levi's available through the mid-sixties. I was discovering something about real USA button-front Levi's in the process of clearing out George's dirty kecks.

As a sartorial aside, a cache of American-made button-front 501s turned up in a Croydon boutique about a year after this event, and a friend who happened to be working there sold them at a lovely knocked-down price. It was the genuine article for me from now on.

Alan and I got very close very quickly. We took our first acid trip together. We had been planning it for some time. Ever since 1967 there had been this big deal concerning the question, 'Are you experienced?' Not just the name of a Jimi Hendrix album, but a kind of social division. For me, as with many others, fear was wrapped up with the knowledge that in our culture it was just 'bound to happen' at some point – that is, dropping a tab, taking a trip. So I had put it back for a couple of years. As for Alan, I don't know. He was from a culture of pill-popping, so it might have come more naturally to him. Plus he had acquired a taste for Jimi Hendrix and Bob Dylan. I know that Dylan was pretty big on the early Mod scene, so that didn't surprise me, but I thought at the time that the music may have brought Alan's thinking around to the LSD experience.

Alan scored our trips. In those days acid was sold for 15/- a trip. A normal score might cost 30/-, and this would be two trips. As it was generally a shared experience, it made sense for the drug to be sold in twos. Alan came back to the flat with something about an inch long, ochre coloured, about the shape of half a Matchmaker, those chocolate sticks that come in a long box, only with the substance of crayon. We broke it in two. He said that he had been told it was STP, a new strain, much stronger. In point of fact STP was the street name for DOM, a form of speed with psychedelic qualities. We hadn't been reading the small print in our underground press, or we might have been more cautious. What Alan had in fact scored was enough for four trips, and STP was stronger than LSD to begin with. So you might surmise (correctly) that our first trip was quite an experience. Mostly an evening of intense hallucinations, with wall posters coming to life and playing entire gigs for me. George was out but Chris spent the evening with us – straight – and we couldn't communicate with him at all. I felt pangs of guilt about that, and it was a side to the drug that seemed harsh.

A sidebar: LSD divided those who had from those who hadn't.

That is, while you were actually tripping. The tripper might influence the non-tripper into a form of headiness, a form of contact high, even of heightened awareness, or alternatively the straight person might be totally alienated. Was it this phenomenon that created the 'cool' attitude of the hippy generation? The 'us' and 'them' of it? Either way, it was another classic acid characteristic added to a night in which we seemed to collect the set!

During the evening two other friends called and I held them at the front door, where they appeared as two dancing and giggling foolish gnomes. Looking back, they may have ingested something psychedelic themselves, as one of them couldn't stop remarking on my resemblance to a walrus – I had grown a thick moustache after the move to George's flat.

Alan and I had a pile of about six LPs on my record player (the days of the auto-changer), which included all the stuff we normally were grooving to at the time: the Who, Hendrix, Small Faces, Spooky Tooth, Led Zeppelin, Pink Floyd, *et al*. During the course of the evening we had a visit from Meg, an old-time local Beat we had known for a few years. There was no holding him at the front door.

Meg tended to stroll around the environs in a bright striped blazer and sunglasses at night. At the time he was squatting in a water tower in the middle of Shirley Hills. He had just regained possession of two of his favourite LPs from someone, somewhere. One was Dr John the Night Tripper's *Gris Gris*, at the time about a year old, but new to Alan and me. The sounds on that album blew us away. The other LP was one of Meg's favourites, and seemingly an essential for his Beat lifestyle. It was Charles Mingus, *Oh Yeah*. These two albums replaced our half dozen rock albums on the deck. The Mingus was so scratched that the hissing and frying-bacon sizzle was as loud as the music, but our acid-fried brains separated the noise from the music. As if the scratches just became something like heavy rain outside. Mingus, Mac Rebennack and the STP married to change my way of thinking, musically. What we had been playing during the STP trip was basically all rock, heavy rock, blues rock. And all that rock went out the figurative window when I heard Mingus and the mellow funk of Dr John. I don't think it affected Alan in the same way at all.

The very next evening I had an audition with a group to go to. I was still tripping, flocks of birds appearing out of my left field of vision as I engaged the outside world on my way to the rehearsal.

Alan had painted throughout the trip. One of his themes, perhaps his main theme, was that of wolfmen. That is, these figures that seemed to come from a very early age, somewhat mythical, with long robes and finery, with the heads of wolves. Alan painted many pictures featuring scenes with these wolf people, and he believed he had known and lived among them in a previous life. I think he may have hung out with them during some of our trips. He used to pronounce them 'woofmen'.

That first trip was around October. At the end of the year I moved out of that flat and Alan moved back in with his mum and dad. I went to a small spare bedroom on the top floor of a little terraced house in Thornton Heath that belonged to a couple: Chris Lansdowne's sister-in-law, June, Holly's sister, and her husband, Roger. Chris and Holly had lived there after they were married. Roger and June were a lovely couple, but I kept to myself and only used the room to store my records, about a hundred and fifty LPs at the time, and my few belongings. Mostly I came in the front door and went straight up to my room. I don't know why I left a thriving scene with lots of people coming and going, and hid myself away, but it was possibly because George was fed up with his painting work getting damaged, and wanting to get back to a simpler scene of living with his girlfriend.

He would not have wanted me to go, but I decided to leave with the bath water, so to speak. Alan was the only person I saw for a while, as we continued being each other's tripping companions. At some point I took a job at Allders department store, and Wednesday was my day off. This necessitated regular acid trips on Tuesday evenings or Wednesdays. Alan and I would roam Croydon and its environs rabbiting ten to the dozen about the world and falling into fits of giggling. There was a lot of very giggly acid around. We were together when I did my Christmas shopping that year. We had a falling to the floor giggling fit in the toiletries department of Allders where I was buying presents. On Christmas day Dad was nonplussed by the tinted face powder I gave him, which I thought was aftershave.

A funny thing happened to me at the end of one of these trips. The guy in whose house I was lodging, Chris L.'s brother-in-law, Roger, had taken up creating light shows. They had all been part of Formula Four when they had supported Pink Floyd and a galaxy of underground stars at a University College midsummer ball a couple of years before. Roger had been impressed with the Floyd's light show, and decided to build his own. He got a very good show together, despite the irony that he and his wife, June, were very straight, and I'm not sure if they really got the 'heady' ramifications of the liquid light effect. Anyway, his light show was so good, he got a few gigs doing it, rather like a guy with a PA or a DJ might get gigs now.

He would try out his lights in the evening sometimes, after work. He would set the slide projector with the cells in the narrow hallway and use the entire hall, landing, stairs and walls as his 'show'. Coming home one early evening at the end of a day tripping with Alan, I walked through the front door straight into the centre of a full-on liquid light show. Somewhere among the colours was Roger playing music and laughing as I tried to engage the stairs. He had no idea.

Meanwhile, Alan had arrived back at his parents' house. They had split up without either of them moving out, and they lived in separate rooms. Alan's dad lived in the front room, and had become a communist in his older years. Mrs Male was a Bohemian who painted, kept Alan's room just as it was, and even had a dinner ready for him during times he lived elsewhere. Now he was back, but only temporarily, he wanted them to know. On his return on this particular night he stumbled through the front door, upon which his dad said loudly from the front room, 'There's Alan on those pills again.' The great kick Alan and I got out of this was the irony of his dad thinking Alan was still stumbling home after a 'block-up'. We were wandering in another reality, and these straights . . . well, you get the idea.

* * *

During the mayhem at Addiscombe I had continued to persue a musical career. I was still auditioning for groups. Having placed another ad in *Melody Maker* I made the mistake of having a completely unknown group who had contacted me pick up my drum kit from the flat. I had been given an address on the phone of a pub in Brixton to turn up at and audition with the group the following evening. When I got to the pub the people there had never heard of the group or ever seen a drum kit. Oh dear. My Premier kit that I'd had throughout the sixties was gone forever. What a fool I was to think that people using the guise of music would be trustworthy. And now Brixton had done for me!

One of the auditions I went to, shortly after my kit had been stolen, was for a local muscan called Mick Roberts, and was held at his friend, Matthew Fisher's house in South Croydon. I got Dad to drive me there, but I kept the loss of my kit a secret from him. At the time Fisher was the organist in Procol Harum, and had written the famous organ line in 'A Whiter Shade of Pale'. He was helping his friend find musicians and was playing guitar. He called for a Beatles song that I didn't know from Adam, and when I didn't play it right, he got moody and stopped talking to or

188

looking at me, letting Roberts know that this audition was over. Thanks for being such a thoroughly nice guy, Matthew Fisher.

Chris R. was my ally in most of the musical ideas that flowed during that year. We would arrange jam sessions that took place at a unique house near to Fairfield Hall in Croydon. It was called 'The Studio', and was owned by a lovely old lady who had antiques strewn throughout the place. The room she rented out for groups was on the ground floor in the front, and it too was littered with precious antiques. Many fun get-togethers were organised there.

I had also kept up with Chris L. Holly was pregnant with their first child. She was desperate to get a group going, but she knew she wouldn't be able to drum, so she would sing while I played drums. Chris L. was going to learn bass, and I recruited Chris R. to play guitar and sing harmonies. The group that would have brought the two Chris's together never happened but Chris L. did help me finance a wonderful Ludwig drum kit, after my Premiers were stolen, for which he was the guarantor.

* * *

The year at the Addiscombe flat was also my most promiscuous year to date. Desiree had found out where I was and gave me a call. I was surprised to hear from her after the mess I'd caused two years before, but she wanted to see me. She came over to the flat, the first in a new series of secret trysts. She had turned seventeen, and Desiree wanted to consummate our love. In secret. The act of loving consent happened at her older and more responsible sister's flat. It was a conspiracy and her sister was in on it.

Desiree and I went out for a while, but although I was a serial monogamist, I had by now a short attention span, and I got to that familiar point again and wanted to move on. Her mother found out (again) and went ballistic. I got an angry phone call that I had to listen to and say, yeah, ruined her life, I know. Sorry 'bout that. Desiree was seventeen, and there was little her mother could do. Desiree's life was not ruined, however. She married, had children, and went on to a successful academic career that included that of author.

Whenever I hear 'The Wind Cries Mary' by Jimi Hendrix I think of Desiree.

Talking of seventeen, my next girlfriend that lovely summer was the same age, but remained intact while she was with me. I wrote her a goodbye letter. She did tell me much later in life that my letter was dragged out of her blazer pocket the following morning by her teacher and read out to her class as an example of well-constructed English. How am I doing?

For the next three years my girlfriends would be short-lived interludes that arrived and left in a blur.

There's One in Every Town

I needed to get out of that room in Thornton Heath. I was still hanging (and tripping) out with Alan and we had started to hang much of the time with a little guy called Burmese Sun. Sun had become a regular caller at the flat in Addiscombe around the same time as Meg. He was actually from Singapore. His story was that he had left there in a hurry at the age of fourteen, on the run from local gangsters. No-one seemed to know what he had been doing for the decade or so in England before he had started to appear around Croydon. He was a little older than us, tiny in stature, with jet black hair almost to his waist. Sun was a low-key pot connection.

At the end of 1969, when I was still renting that little room on my own, Sun had started to hook up with a girl he was keen on, Linda. Linda was sixteen and had run away from wherever home was a year previously. She hung out with an older friend called Terri, who had become her guardian. The two girls were living in a flat in Crystal Palace, and Sun asked me to come over there with him one evening; he had a favour he wanted of me. Basically, he had been working on cementing something with Linda, and she was always with Terri. So, guess what, he wanted me to 'take care' of Terri.

This led to a very awkward evening, involving long silences and sideways glances. Our problem was that I thought Linda was way more 'my type' than Terri. That meant that I could not under any circumstances 'get off' with someone who I didn't fancy, while someone to whom I owed *nothing* made friends with the one I fancied. Both girls were lovely about the situation, knowing what was going on, as women will, and probably saved their chuckles until we'd gone.

So nothing happened that night, leaving Sun a mite frustrated. Sometime after this double date, Sun and Linda became an item, I don't know how he managed it. I never saw Terri again, though. And Linda had told Sun about this house on Tamworth Road in West Croydon, where she and Terri had lived for a while. Sun told me about it just as I was getting anxious to move.

* * *

Tamworth Road at the time was famous, or infamous, for the Bentley/Craig case. At the end of 1952, two boys named Bentley and Craig took a bus from that sleepy burg Norbury, on the London Road, on their way to burgle Barlow & Parker's wholesale confectioners. They climbed to the warehouse roof, a policeman was shot dead – and the rest is history. The older Bentley, a youth with arrested mental powers, was sent to the gallows in place of his friend, Craig, who was too young to hang. It was a twisted and corrupt fit-up between the police and the judicial system, symptomatic of the tight-arse English fifties. It took decades for Bentley to get a pardon, too late for his mum. As a boy growing up in the fifties, especially in the borough where it happened, the case would linger as a warning to later generations. I have to say that its terrible influence on local mothers was strongest. For instance, it may have added to my own mother's strong over-protectiveness, and her need to 'screen' any of my friends that came knocking. In other households of working-class south London, you might have heard the warning to wayward boys, 'You'll bloody 'ang, you will!' A year later I would write a piece on the Bentley/Craig case for Jamie Reid's *Suburban Press*.

The house in Tamworth Road had been bought, probably for a song, by a guy called Johnny Hawkins, who was the lead guitarist in a rock 'n' roll revival band called the Wild Angels. Johnny was South African, and sported a dreadful version of a rock 'n' roll hairdo, a precursor of the seventies mullet. It was long at the back, with the sides thinned out so they could be swept back, with a quiff in the front. His long-suffering girlfriend did the cutting and thinning. Come to think of it, she may have styled all the Wild Angels.

The house had a basement, ground, first and second floors. Johnny lived in one room at the front on the ground floor with his girlfriend, a very nice person. The only other room on the ground floor was a kitchen, which served as a bathroom for anyone interested in bathing (there was no actual bathroom in the house). There was a WC on the ground floor too, which we all had to share.

I should mention the basement. This was one square room of incredible squalor. Damp, filthy and badly lit. The walls were lined with dirty mattresses for soundproofing, as the Wild Angels used the room for practice. Johnny also rented the basement out to local groups, but one thing I do know for sure. A few months before I moved in, the Wild Angels had rehearsed in Johnny's basement with Gene Vincent, for a tour they embarked on together. The Vincent rehearsals are captured in a documentary film about that tour, the penultimate tour Gene ever undertook on this side of the Atlantic. He did another in 1971, the year he died of a bleeding ulcer in suburban California. One thing that documentary cannot give you, as sad as it is, is the feeling of utter despair one could feel in that disgusting cellar. This before adding to it the fact that one of the most important artists of all time was forced by circumstances actually to climb down to this level.

I went round to see Johnny very early in 1970. He showed me up to the back first-floor room, not that big but not *too* small.

Sun met me round there; I didn't know why until I was viewing the room.

Johnny said, 'That'll be £4 per week.'

I said, 'That'll be fine.'

Then Sun edged his way passed me, looked at the room, and said, 'Yeah, we'll take it.' Johnny, looking as surprised as myself, said, 'Oh, if there're two of you it'll be £8. I was renting to one, but I don't mind, but it'll be double.'

Why did I not say, 'Yeah, I thought it was just me too!'?

Anyway, Sun and I moved in. Two single mattresses and not much else in the way of space. Actually I owned the only stuff we moved in. I had the record player, records (out of bounds to anyone but myself), not a lot else. I had a bookshelf that Mum had made me at some point, in black wood, and I placed that out on the first floor landing with my (then) meagre collection of paperbacks on it. How did I stop people from taking them? Too stoned to read?

It was enlightening to then find that Linda was moving in with us. Johnny discovered this about the same time I did. So, he said, 'That'll be £12 then.' Sun complained, thought Johnny was a hustler. Why didn't I say, he's no hustler, and I don't want to live with you and your bird, either? It was all par for the course then; it was communal living.

We settled in. Alan became a fixture. In fact, frankly, he moved in, it was just that he had to sleep on the floor. With him on the floor there was no room to spare when we were all asleep. Johnny knew Alan was there and wanted another £4 per week, which he never got. That really was hustling.

Now, our floor had a large room in the front, which was rented by one man on his own: the one and only Meg. It did seem odd – the room was huge, while four of us were packed into the back room. Meg spent a lot of time in our room, however. He was a total freeloader. He would appear when he thought there might be a taste of something to smoke, which there always was. We would occasionally build a joint with live match heads rolled into it, and get him to light it. Bang! Bang! Fzzz! He never sussed it, and we kept doing it. He was so spaced out, just thought it was a weird thing to happen to him.

Meg had shoulder-length dark brown hair and a black beard, with orb-like hazel eyes that lived somewhere between kindness and spaceyness. Some nights he would arrive wearing his striped blazer and sunglasses, an outfit that had become his normal mode of dress. He would have been for a long ramble. Would regale us with stories of how many flying saucers he had seen on his way. Actually the number he'd see grew as the weeks went by. But Meg seemed to get more morose as time went on at Tamworth Road. His old happy self was replaced by a character finding more to moan about than positivity. Those pale brown eyes were looking troubled. One day we spotted a notice on his door that said, 'Gone for a long walk.' We never saw Meg again. A Croydon legend gone.

On the top floor there was a similar situation. A bunch of young heads crammed into the back room, a slightly younger generation of Croydon potheads whom we had less to do with. There were only two years between us, but somehow we made it count. It was a kind of generation gap. Just like the guys on the Beat scene had looked down on us. In the front room was a guy called Dave, a sharper character than the rest of the residents at Tamworth, a bit 'spivvy' in a way, a real hustler, someone who was more about 'birds' than flying. The owner of a purple Volkswagen Beach Buggy that was parked in a small car park opposite the house. Kind of a misfit in a way. That is, a misfit by the standards of the house in Tamworth Road! Dave had little to do with anyone else in the house. Johnny Hawkins' girlfriend couldn't wait to hang out with the hippy tenants as soon as the Wild Angels were off on tour. When this happened the house got a little wilder.

A fair amount of acid was going down at Tamworth Road. The four of us in the little room shared more than one lysergic evening, with a paraffin heater making patterns for us on the ceiling. I had my routine of tripping on Tuesdays as I had Wednesday off from the food department. Silly of me to imagine for one minute that Alan was sticking to the same regime. Ha. On the other days, various people might be hanging out in our tiny space, going out of their tiny minds. For instance, one evening I came in, straight, and a young girl was having a bad time on acid, surrounded by concerned 'helpers'. I had a full red beard at the time and had taken to dressing as a clone of Lee Marvin in *The Wild One*. I had gone up to Portobello Road to get a striped sweatshirt from an outfitters that is long gone. The denims were unwashed and stood to attention by my bed. The boots were hobnail chic.

This girl was freaked out, she thought I was a wolf or a bear or something. Trouble was I thought it was a cheek not being able to stroll into my own place. I sat around in Meg's room until she had been calmed down and had left. But, as I said, those were the times. One evening I came home in a filthy mood, one of *my* LPs was on *my* record player, which I removed from the deck without lifting the tone arm. Helluva noise. Helluvan impression.

* * *

At this time the Star Hotel was still the place to hang out. The bands appearing were slightly lower on the ladder than they had been, including many local outfits. We saw one of David Bowie's early groups there, among others. I also met and joined my last group for many years at the Star during those months. We were called Dwarf and when we split that summer, I called it a day with being a musician for some years. I was tired of the endless build up and let down. The notion of being a pure Beat was exerting more of a pull on me now. The local venue that took the place of the Star was the Greyhound, on the ground floor of a tower block opposite Fairfield Hall. This was still going strong when I finally left the burg less than two years later. Meanwhile, we hung out there, and also saw, if we wanted to pay the price of a ticket, the Faces, Humble Pie and Free, to name some of the more regular and most enjoyable live bands of the time, and on one occasion Detroit's MC5, who would gather more significance for me over the following year.

Up West

Sun was very particular about where he scored his hash. This involved going up to the West End in a Mini that Sun had acquired. We would do weekly runs up to a pub called the Frigate, which was on St Martin's Lane, Covent Garden, in London's theatreland. This old Victorian pub had been gutted without a thought to its history, renamed the Frigate and turned into a three-level mock-up of an old dockyard. The resulting interior meant you could enjoy your drink whilst watching sailors' kit bags being hoisted up and down to the sounds of squeaking pulleys!

Outside, poking obtrusively into the West End foot traffic, was a lady figurehead seemingly lashed to the front of a ship. There was a bit of a folk scene here, too. We once saw Don Partridge performing 'Rosie, Oh Rosie' to a handful of devotees in the basement. Right opposite was another pub called the Sussex, on Long Acre, which was boring by comparison but gained fame for being bombed by the IRA in the seventies. Don't look for the Frigate today: it has gone the same way that original Victorian boozer went before it.

At the Frigate we would meet a rough gentleman by the name of Bard, an old connection of Sun's, and from Bard we scored, and then drove back to West Croydon. At some point Bard changed his location to Notting Hill Gate. Not Portobello or anywhere around the Grove mind you, but actually at Notting Hill. In fact, the upstairs room of a pub called the Devonshire Arms, right along from the Tube station. Another pub it would be pointless to look for today, as it's now an estate agent. Bard appeared to be dwelling in one of the small but expensive houses behind the Classic Cinema, which seemed an inappropriately expensive area for him even then. Many years later I would see Bard as a regular at the old Warwick Castle on Portobello, an establishment that had acquired the height of seediness at the time. When seeing one morning that the pub's windows had all been smashed the previous night, a closer inspection clearly showed them to have been smashed from the *inside*. A much more appropriate place for our man, Bard. But I'm getting ahead of myself.

Back at Tamworth Road, Sun would lay our piece of precious bounty between two out-of-use cupboard doors on the floor, and then proceed to walk up and down stamping on the top door. When Alan and I first saw this we had to ask, 'What the fuck are you doing?' Sun's enigmatic reply was that he was still being hassled for little quid deals by local potheads, and this way our weighed hash was uncompromised by a little sharing. Sun himself had quit dealing, and we were not about to start, but the door method was one of Sun's funniest tricks.

One day the other guys went up west to score. When they got back they delivered the bad news: they had got ripped off. They looked glum, it was the end of our investment. Shortly after this we all moved out of Tamworth Road. Sun and Linda moved to Cornwall. Alan continued to be Alan around Croydon, a figure whose legend grew over the years. As for me, word had got around that there was a new house opening up. I looked into it.

Up a Steep Hill

Downs Court Road is in a very salubrious part of Purley, Surrey. The house was called 'Morpeth'. Right opposite was a very steep hill down to the Godstone Road, which was a hoot going down but a sweat coming back. The hill is listed as 14 per cent, which is considered by many previous residents as an underestimate. It includes a sharp bend near the bottom too. There was a sign at this end reading '1 in 7 Hill'. Most visitors to, and residents of, Morpeth used another way.

There were four girls renting the house from a family who were away for a defined period. At an early stage two of the girls had left, replaced quickly by Johnny Blunt and his old mate, Tommy. Tommy hailed from Monks Hill and had hung out at Addiscombe for a while. The family had rented to four girls, but once Johnny and Tommy arrived it seemed the floodgates had opened.

I found out about the place through Bob 'n' Hilary, two old and dear friends who had recently become one, and had moved into a room on the ground floor. Bob was also from Monks Hill, and I had first met him back in the Heathfield Road days in South Croydon. He was a buddy of Chris Reeves and Maurice. Hilary, by contrast, was a renegade who had worked at Biba, from where she had descended, hippy-clad, on our little scene at Addiscombe, going out with George the Painter for a while. For which we had all considered him so lucky he might have walked through shit and ended up smelling of the proverbial roses.

By the time I moved in Tommy had gone to Cornwall with

Sun and Linda. I moved into a temporary situation, with Bob 'n' Hilary asking me to hang on for a while as a good room would soon be coming free. What was this temporary situation? Basically, the two ladies who still rented the house were sharing a large double bedroom on the first floor. These girls were groupies. Not flat-out, all-the-way, all-the-time groupies, but more music fans who were out every night of the week at one gig or another, ligging. Somehow I was offered the arrangement of using their room during the night, and so I moved in. I have no idea what I did with all my stuff in the meantime. I would climb into this huge double bed after the usual evening of being out or sitting round the house with whoever was there at the time, and awaken sometime in the early hours as the two girls returned home and climbed in either side of me. There would then be an hour or so before I had to rise and get off to work (I had gone back to that farm I had worked on back in 1967), the cool of the morning being warmed by the bodies either side, and on the other hand, my fellow bedmates enjoying the benefits of a pre-warmed bed.

The room was full of the girls' ephemera, including well-thumbed copies of *Oz* magazine, seemingly their only reading material. I did get invited to one gig with them, which was at the Lyceum. This was to see an American outfit called Flock, who I thought were so-so, American prog rock being more boring than the English variety. Backstage we hob-nobbed with the likes of Mick Taylor (who made me think of my Chelsea days) and Keith Emerson (he of the Nice), names that by a strange twist of fate have already appeared in my story. I was impressed by how many people these girls had got to know.

Anyway, I aimed to take the first room that became available in the house. I liked the arrangement with the groupies but I wanted autonomy. There was a small nursery room also on the first floor. It had Dilly Duckling wallpaper, and I already had in mind the perverse idea of mixing and matching my Peter Fonda in *The Wild Angels* poster with the wallpaper. Plus the idea of a small room seemed to preclude any possibility of sharing at any point. Bob 'n' Hilary said why not wait for a better room, but I was determined. So that became my room.

Let me take you around Morpeth. The ground floor had a large sitting room in which general partying would take place. I seem to remember that eventually so many people wanted to move in, the sitting room became someone's room. Behind the sitting room was a large kitchen and dining room, with a back door. This room also hosted many social goings on. For most of my tenure at the house Bob 'n' Hilary had prepared huge pots of home-mixed muesli, which we literally lived on, this coinciding with my becoming a veggie. Sometime in the early part of this year, during my tripping days with Alan, I had found myself staring into the illuminated display of a butcher's window one night, on my own, after Alan had gone his own way. Though it's hard to convey precisely the feeling of devastating horror working in my brain at the tail end of that trip, suffice it to say I became a lifelong vegetarian.

The kitchen seemed to be the domain of a chap named Demented Dan. Dan enjoyed roaming the house in the nude, and even answered the front door to my mother like this once. His impeccable manners impressed so well, Mum failed to notice Dan's bollocks. Dan loved to instigate jam sessions. He would kick something off by asking me to drum on some pots and pans, while he mostly rendered Cliff Richard's 'Move It!' These kitchen jams were timeless.

Bob 'n' Hilary lived in a room at the back, with French doors that opened onto the garden. Their room was immediately the one with the coolest vibe. I installed my trusty one-piece stereo in there, while my LPs lived safely up in my nursery. Now, the odd thing about Morpeth is that the place attracted strangers from the farthest corners of the world. A side passage ran along the left-hand wall of the house and into the garden. Most people who knew us all would use this passage and enter through Bob 'n' Hilary's room. This would eventually lead to them locking the French doors when the intrusion got to be a little too much. One day a total stranger walked through the French doors with, 'At last. Thank God I found it.' To which Bob 'n' Hilary, open-mouthed, graciously made the man coffee and made him feel at home.

On another occasion two of Hilary's oldest friends walked in. One was Chillum Jeff, who had recently returned from India, his companion that night being Rory Fellowes, who later found some TV fame with stop-time animation on Hattytown, and with the Clive Barker films. Jeff had once been Hilary's boyfriend, but back before I knew her, back in the days when they were crazy Mods and she was Jeff's scooter ornament. He had been to India for a long time, and picked up a morphine habit of epic proportions. A near-death illness that had put him in hospital had started the junk habit, and he had returned to Blighty to kick it, which he had. The residual was a mammoth intake of high-quality weed, and a lifelong love affair with needles. The two guys flopped onto Bob 'n' Hilary's bed, much to Bob 'n' Hilary's consternation, and afterwards Jeff did in fact move into the house for the duration of its rental time.

Bob and I got a job shortly after I moved in. It was with a temp agency that placed a whole team of ne'er-do-wells with a record distribution company called Phonodisc, owned by Philips. The job was over in Edmonton, and involved the two of us rising early. Dexedrine, the yellow tablet known as 'Mother's Little Helper', was a popular 'upper' at the time – in fact, I'd been using them off and on since living at Tamworth.

Okay, here's the morning scenario. Before turning in for the night Bob would line up 'Desolation Row' by Bob Dylan on my gramophone, which resided in his 'n' Hilary's room. The record player was powered by the electric ceiling light, and the switch was at the end of the bed. Bob 'n' Hilary's alarm would ring at an ungodly hour and Bob would sit up and turn on the light switch. This would kick in Dylan's lengthy ode and in turn raise Bob from the bed. Bob 'n' Hilary Bob, not Dylan Bob. He would have some Dexies ready at his bedside and would ingest them at the point of moving into the kitchen. He would then make coffee for two, and bring mine up to the nursery, with some water and two or three Dexies, all on a tray. I would swallow the pills and lie there waiting for them to kick in. And they did, and when they did the coffee would be cool enough to sip, and I'd pull on some clothes. Neat, really. By the time we reached north London some hours later we would be speeding and would then down a huge fry-up at a greasy café. I wonder if all that might have affected our health?

But let me get back to taking you around the house. The garden was the domain of two men, both residents, but disparate individuals. One was called Len, another of the Monks Hill brigade, and he had moved into a shed in the garden. Once every few weeks he would clean the house from top to bottom. He would take some Dexies, wet his long blond hair, comb it back, and go to work. He did this because no-one else ever did anything. He didn't even live in the house itself. The other chap was named Terry, a chiropodist. He was also the possessor of a gigantic medical book, which was his bedtime reading. Terry had discovered all sorts of 'medicines' that grow in the wild, and was researching how to recognise them. The garden at Morpeth became his pharmacy, and he knew what he was doing!

So let's climb the stairs. First room at the top was Johnny Blunt's domain. Johnny tended to keep to himself. There was a bathroom, the bedroom I had shared with the girls, and the small nursery room I moved into. If there were other chambers, and doubtless there were, then they have receded into the mists caused by the nefarious activity common to most nights there.

There was some extremely potent LSD on the market at this time. Pretty much everyone at Morpeth tripped out. Possibly because of the nature of the amount of people around, most trips would be complicated by this in some way. I do well remember one trip in particular. When I say I remember the trip, I suppose I mean my trip, Bob 'n' Hilary's trip, John's trip. It is easy to confuse one trip with another, that's the nature of the beast. But I think I have all the parts of one trip in one place.

There really did seem to be a number of us at the house, not all residents, who had dropped a tab. It was an occasion when John was looning around with the rest of us, and I for one was definitely having a good time. John did something very physical like leap over his car parked outside, doing himself some damage. It appeared that he had discovered a flagon of cider in the fridge and refreshed himself with some deep quaffs as the acid was taking hold. We tried to keep outside activity to a minimum, as we were aware of the neighbours not being too enamoured with the 'hippies' occupying the other half of this large, semi-detached house. Somewhere along the night John's trip turned on him, and he ended up being talked down by Hilary in the back room. This left Bob 'n' I together, being very philosophical about all and sundry. Maybe too philosophical – I slipped into an uncontrollable paranoia, a sort of confusion, which took the devil of a time to get out of.

Bob, I think, helped me. Bob 'n' Hilary, doctors and nurses for the night. It's almost impossible to describe the confusion I felt, my mind sliding out of my control, a lost hopeless feeling. Shortly after this I had the same feeling at our place of work, just reacting to something said. It's a feeling that has remained part of my make-up, and needs constant checking. Who knows. Can you affect a part of your brain, uncover something that's usually in check, twist something loose? Should we have never tripped in such surroundings, with so many people? I had always had private trips with one companion, usually Alan. I never suffered from fearsome hallucinations, but that trip included a section that was definitely related to mental illness. And it seemed to be going round.

An arrival at Morpeth one day was Pete Lieberman, the talented guitarist I had first met back in the Rosalyn days, and who I had been in Blues Caravan with. Pete had been a star at Bristol University since I had last seen him. While he was there the hallucinogens that we were all using at the time had played a rude trick on Pete. By the time he was at Morpeth he was working an ice-cream van for a living. According to Pete, he witnessed some kind of post-nuclear holocaust one day while he was slinging cornets. He spent some time in Bob 'n' Hilary's wardrobe until he was better. B 'n' H to the rescue again. Last I heard about Pete, he had changed his name by deed poll.

Morpeth came to an end at the close of the summer. I was not there at the very end, but I heard that when the owners came round to collect the keys and move back in, the lady of the family actually burst into tears when she saw the house. As the saying went, never trust a hippy.

* * *

In 1970 I played with my last band for a number of years, known as Dwarf. One of the gigs that Dwarf did was opening for East of Eden at Carshalton College. I had no idea that this was a Commercial Entertainments promotion – my old agents! – until *decades* later when I found an ad in the back of an old *Melody Maker*. I wonder if I'd have searched around for Tony Cousins, the man we used to beg money from in Denmark Street, if I'd known? I had met the other members of Dwarf at the Star. The songwriter, lead guitarist and singer was called Gerry, and when the band split Gerry asked me to come over to the bass player's house, where our rehearsals took place, and help him record his entire repertoire of songs onto a tape recorder.

I never knew why he wanted to do this until I discovered that Gerry later sold the publishing rights to the songs we had performed for a considerable sum of money. He went on to join what was to become the Glitter Band, meaning for much of the seventies I would see little Gerry on TV dressed in shiny silver outfits and playing a star-shaped guitar! By that time I was getting back into playing music but seeing Gerry always reminded me that his little taping episode had persuaded me to give up the music biz, as it had been one occasion too many where another's intentions were aided by me without my knowledge of what the hell was going on.

In stepping away from music for the next few years I gave up my last chance of making any impression in the business. I was the right age at twenty-two, it was the right time, yet what I wanted to do was pull back from that scene, try to figure what it was I really wanted, and find another path. I sold my Ludwig kit, that great kit that Chris L. had helped me get a credit arrangement for the previous year. Trouble was, I had not finished paying for it, by a long shot! Vaguely I recall a visit around at Morpeth from a representative of the hire purchase company. When someone is your guarantor you cannot just drift off and leave them to sort it out. I paid up, and in the doing said goodbye to drumming for four years.

In 1969 and 1970 England really took the rock festival to heart. I had not bothered to follow Alan to the Isle of Wight in '69 when we were at Addiscombe, but the two of us went together for the Bath Festival of '70, which was the first really big festival of its kind held in the UK. It was at a place called Shepton Mallet, and I can still picture Alan and myself tramping along with hundreds of others, having hitched our way to Somerset. We spent a lot of our time in a large communal tent, and we spotted Linda and Sun, who had made their way from Cornwall.

The line-up was an incredible who's who of the rock business: Pink Floyd doing their usual dawn thing, Johnny Winter with Jeff Beck as a guest, Jefferson Airplane, Frank Zappa with the Mothers of Invention reformed for the occasion, the Byrds, Country Joe & the Fish, Led Zeppelin, Fairport Convention, Santana, John Mayall re-joined by Peter Green, Canned Heat, Steppenwolf, the list goes on and on.

Our friend Dr John the Night Tripper came on and, I swear, made it rain. It rained, seriously, for a few hours. Thousands of us huddling in tents or soaking outside under blankets and makeshift shelter. Bath was the first festival of its kind for me, and, as it turned out, the last.

A Cask of Amontillado

The Royal Oak in Croydon closed its doors sometime in 1968, an early indication of the rampant redevelopment that would one day engulf the entire town, burying its former character under a deluge of ominous square blocks of concrete and glass. By the time the damage was done, and the old town had disappeared from view, or even *existence*, I had long gone.

But when the Royal Oak closed down its Bohemian clientele strolled across Surrey Street to a pub almost opposite called the Dog & Bull. This was more what you'd call a market pub, the stallholders having used it for generations. A little rough around the edges, though clean, tidy and very Olde Worlde charming, there was always an edge of something likely to go off at any time at the Dog & Bull. Most of us Bohemian types had completely ignored the pub until it seemed the obvious place to replace the Oak, although some of my friends had been slipping across the road occasionally before the Oak closed its doors. There was a square room in the back away from the bar, which itself was four-sided and could serve from any of its sides. Above the bar was an area of cross beams that housed barrels, and some early newcomer had discovered what was in them: a wine known as Amontillado.

Amontillado is a variety of sherry, named for the Montilla region of Spain, and fortified to approximately 17.5 percent alcohol. To us, circa 1969, it was just thick, oaky red wine that seemed more like port. But it was strong. It was not something

I for one ordered at the bar on every visit. It would sometimes just take my fancy, or maybe someone else's fancy. A pint of ale, a glass or two of Amontillado, and back to the ale. And you were going off your rocker.

'The Cask of Amontillado' is also a short story by Edgar Allen Poe first published in November 1846. The story is set in a nameless Italian city in an unspecified year, possibly in the eighteenth century, and is about the narrator's deadly revenge on a friend whom he believes has insulted him. Like several of Poe's stories, and in keeping with the nineteenth-century fascination with the subject, the narrative revolves around a person being buried alive, in this case by immurement. Probably very much like being immured in Croydon.

My main companions over the following few years at the Dog & Bull would be my old mates, Chris Reeves, still very much in the music scene I had left behind (he was in fact working for a group who had had one hit, called Rock Candy, and treading the boards for an agent rather like my own Commercial Entertainments, his being named Starlight Artists); Maurice, still a student at Chelsea but hanging at the local pub a little more; Droopy; George the Painter, unchanged, as he would continue to be; a couple known as Fred 'n' Lucy; and another couple, this time both men, known as the Two Jacks. This was because both their names were Jack.

Now, of course, there were many more regulars than this, in fact most of the local hippie/Beat/head population, but my memory allows only these names for the time being. What I remember most about the back room is almost constant discussion, descending at times into bickering. The Two Jacks were the main thrust of intellectual banter, but it amounted mostly to sarcasm at the expense of anyone who happened to be in the firing line. Chris R. and Maurice would often be the main opponents of the Two Jacks. One other thing about the Two Jacks is that they were the first young men I knew who were confirmed alcoholics. This was at a time when most of my friends were mainly concerned with recreational drugs, and even though some of them would go in the direction of alcohol abuse in the years that followed, the Two Jacks were ahead of the game. I remember they took a holiday one year and went abroad somewhere; they did everything together. Upon their return, after much questioning about their experience, it transpired they had sat in a local bar for the entire vacation.

There was always an element of rough locals at the Dog & Bull. When in our cups we tried not to let our discussion bleed over to include any of the locals at any time. Sometimes there would be a slip-up, however. On one occasion Maurice received a savage kicking outside. I'm sure he thought he had been having an intellectual debate until he left the pub.

In the eighties some of us held a reunion at the pub. The old crowd was no longer there, except for George the Painter, who seemed to have blended into the oak panelling. He had also suffered a stroke and was limp on one side, a fact that made me want to go easy on him in response to his immediate sarcasm upon our arrival, as if he had last seen me just the week before. That same night, after we had had quite a few drinks, the conversation spread out to include some of the locals, in a way we had always used to avoid. Someone with us was unaware of the protocol. We ended the evening running up Surrey Street to escape a fight.

Balham – Gateway to the South

I spent some time after Morpeth laying my head wherever there was a bed or some floor space, one example being the floor belonging to Cretin O'Day. Cretin, though quite upper-middle-class and privileged, was a guy the same age as me, with long blond hair, who had been stranded by his parents after his schooling when they decided to move, and, left to his own devices, had strayed into some weird areas.

At one time that blond hair was streaked with a dirty brown that was in fact dried blood. A gang of Hells Angels had beaten him up outside a café in East Croydon and he had instructed the hospital to not cut his hair when they put the stitches in. His main kicks were necromancy and sorcery, which he was quite serious about. His pad was one room, with a little partitioned-off kitchen space, shared with a large rat. His nearest neighbour, across the hall, was a Bible freak who once caught me alone and, elbowing his way into Cretin's room, lectured me on the subject of Cretin being the Antichrist. I didn't know who was the madder.

One afternoon the landlord came round with some heavies, and I was unfortunately there on my own again. They spent some time intimidating me, until the landlord started to demonstrate how hard he was by kicking up the rug. It was his way of saying, look what a mess we have here. The kicked-over rug exposed Cretin's pentagram chalked on the lino, and the landlord's eyes bulged. He was from Eastern European stock and he recognised something from the Old Country. He knocked his heavies out of the way in his hurry to flee Cretin's hell.

Towards the end of 1970 Bob 'n' Hilary invited me to move in to a place they'd found in Balham, and I couldn't wait to get up off Cretin's pentagrammed floor. Endlesham Road was a two-roomed flat on the ground floor in a Victorian terrace, very close to Balham railway station and the Northern line. This meant that I had easy access to Croydon and just as easy access to town. I started frequenting Portobello Road more, taking orders for fur coats from heads in Croydon, buying up half a dozen on the 'Bello, and selling them later. Blame John Lennon for that style direction. We had our own bathroom across the hall, and the back room was meant to be a diner-kitchen, but I made camp on a single truckle bed in there, so it was a kitchen/bedroom. Bob 'n' Hilary had the front room, and that is where my trusty one-piece stereo lived for the next few months. The bathroom was where Bob 'n' Hilary made candles.

The candles led to our being present at a free festival organised by David and Angela Bowie, but mainly by Angela, as she tended to organise most of David's career around this time, at Martin's Fields in Bromley on American Independence Day (a coincidence), where Bob 'n' Hilary set up a candles stall. An old friend of mine called Noël was playing that day, and, I believe, managed to blow up David's amp. Some of us had been regulars at the Beckenham Arts Lab the previous year, which David used to run, and Noël had played with the future superstar there. This free festival appeared to be an unmitigated disaster for all kinds of reasons, yet we all ended up back at Haddon Hall in Beckenham, David and Angela's place, for bonhomie and hanging out. David and Hilary had a lengthy discussion about the Incredible String Band and possibly Taoism. They also had a mutual friend in Rory Fellowes, whom Bob and I only knew from the Morpeth days. Bob and I got hugely stoned.

In September the bombshell of Jimi Hendrix's death stunned everyone I knew. Bob 'n' I were in Ilford that day – we still had our job with Phonodisc, and by now we were travelling to the Ilford branch. We were on to a good thing. Until we got busted.

* * *

It was a case of a bent security guard who was on duty during the overtime shifts, turning a blind eye to products leaving by the side door during the hours of darkness. Mind you, his blind eye still cost the thieves some money and some of the items. Then someone upset the bent security guard, who felt he did not get what was due him after a night's side-door work. So he ratted. Now, this meant that one night at the end of our night shift, for which Bob had become the foreman, we were stopped by the Ilford police. There had been a mistake.

While these keen officers were interviewing us outside the front door, the real culprits, the ones the bent security guard had ratted on, were busy loading up a van at the side door. Now, Bob 'n' I had a few LPs tucked nicely in our overcoats, and although we had to go through a formality at the station, these keen officers understood by then that they had made the mistake of missing the real heist.

Our few bits up our coats meant I had to be taken back to Balham to inspect the premises and offer up a few other stolen bits, which I carefully selected. But the main trouble for me was that a keen officer back at Ilford police station had found a tiny tab of acid in one of my pockets. The arresting officers were not keen on getting involved with this – they had enough on their plates having missed the big heist – but they could not do anything about this one rabid dog who wanted to bust me for drugs.

'Keep that away from him,' said the rabid dog, 'He'll eat it before you know it.' Raised eyebrows all round.

214

So I got out on bail thanks to Mum, about which she was less than pleased – they had taken me back to Ilford police station, and given me a cell for the night, after the free ride to Balham – and I had to go to Barking court at some time in the near future and get a criminal record for theft and possession of dangerous drugs.

I moved out of Endlesham Road SW12 at the end of November 1970; I needed to be on my own again.

Outlaw Blues

Number 125 Selhurst Road, SE25, was a stone's throw from Grandma, and in an area in which I had spent so many happy hours of my childhood. Very soon after I left Balham, Bob 'n' Hilary upped sticks and moved to South Wales. They were the first 'get it together in the country hippies' that I knew. Number 125 was a Morgan Rowland flat (hello again), one tiny room on the first floor at the rear. In one corner was a sink and draining board unit of the cheapest possible manufacture. Over it wobbled a water boiler made of plastic that plugged into a wall socket. I could boil about two pints of water, and that's how I made instant coffee. I had a two-ring electric plate that did for the beans and whatever else could be heated in a saucepan. The vegetarian goes spare again. It was goodbye to Hilary's brown rice and cauliflower cheese.

I had a single bed and a sideboard, my trusty one-piece stereo, LPs in the sideboard, a comic collection and . . . that's all she wrote. I acquired a large orange curtain made of a horrible synthetic bobbly material from my aunty. It covered one whole wall, and gave a sort of impression of something beyond. Well, that was the idea. It was the smallest place I think I ever lived in, but I was on my own, which was good.

I was not alone for long. Alan and I were still hanging out most of the time, and as he was back living with his mum over in Old Town, he spent most nights with me at Selhurst Road. We spent Christmas on our own. I had got used to a discombobulated family and hence no obligation to be anywhere. There was a Boxing Day ritual at my uncle's house, where Dad, my aunty and Grandma and I would gather, and it was the nearest thing to a family Christmas gathering. Mum was always away in the early seventies.

This was the year before Mum and Fred bought a large bungalow in the leafy reaches of Selsdon, coincidentally in the same road where Jean MacColl lived with her daughter, Kirsty, and where I had attended some of those parties a few years before. This meant that starting the following Christmas I was *expected* to spend Christmas Day at the new home. It took me some time to overcome the inner question of, so, what about the few years you were not around, Mum? Since my folks had split up I had become used to the idea of having no Christmas obligation, thank you very much. Why should I be at her beck and call now? It rankled, but I did my duty. I digress.

So on Christmas Day 1970 Alan and I dropped a tab of acid and lurched off in the direction of Lloyds Park, beyond South Croydon. I need to just mention at this point that the piece of land to which I refer is officially Lloyd Park, but for reasons beyond my ken, we always knew it as Lloyds Park (Lloyd's?). I will continue to do so here.

Christmas, of course, is always quiet, and in Croydon in 1970, it was as quiet as the grave. Plus it had snowed heavily. Lloyds Park is a huge expanse of parkland of some natural rolling beauty, still the same today but with a tiny part of one edge robbed by a new tramline.

The park is sort of attached to Shirley Hills, and the two places, with their woods and trails, had been the scene of more than one lysergic adventure. On this Christmas Day the entire park was covered with a layer of virgin white snow. It must be said that it was breathtaking, and would have been even had we not both been peaking on the crest of some Strawberry Fields. Alan and I, two dark stick figures if seen from a distance, traversed the park to and fro for many hours, creating the only footprints for miles for one whole day, a lovely bright day, the day when England's shop is closed. We just could not seem to drag ourselves away.

But eventually we did, although I can't recall the journey back to Selhurst. Back at 125, in that sordid but bright orange room, we made a meal of beans on toast (although I don't remember having a toaster), and huddled around an electric fire, the comedown from the LSD and the room itself causing us both to feel a chill. Some Christmas feast, but we really didn't mind; we felt this was our fitting version of St Nick's Holy Day. The one thing that disturbed us, and in fact was becoming the most pressing experience of the evening, was that both of us were nearly blind! We realised with a nervous chuckle that we had spent a few hours of the day walking with bright white snow beneath us, a fair sun reflected off the ground, both with our faces relaxed in that way that happens on acid, so that trippers always remarked on how young their friends looked on it, with their face muscles dropped, and eyes wide open. That was the point, the eyes wide open. In ordinary circumstances, that many hours in those conditions would call for sunglasses. We were snow blind!

As time went by, others came round to 125. Tanner, Porky and Cowboy to be precise. Three characters from the biker world. We had met up and started hanging at the Star Hotel, still at the time the place for heads of all descriptions most nights in late 1970 – the Greyhound had taken over as a gig, but not immediately as a place to hang. Apparently the close proximity of Thornton Heath Pond had brought these guys down the road to the Star.

Thornton Heath Pond sits on a main junction of the London Road. If the pond hadn't dried up years before it would be in the middle of a roundabout right on the London to Brighton Road. There used to be a tea stall at the Pond. A place where lorry drivers, bikers and various ne'er-do-wells would gather after dark.

Sausage sandwiches and tea constituted the main menu. Hells Angels, hippies, beat groups passing through, would all mingle. Many thousands of nights were spent here by many thousands of people. The man who worked there was called Dave, sometimes The Pie Man. He had a way of making your sandwich and asking, 'Sarce?'

My new mates had been members of one of a myriad of unofficial chapters of Hells Angels that sprang up in England in the late sixties. They had been called the Pond Chapter (ho hum), and the whole thing had ground to a halt some time before. They all still knew each other – some of them were still bad boys around Croydon, some still hung out at the Pond, which some of my friends also did. Maybe that was the connection. This small group of breakaway bikers were altogether more druggy than their fellow ex-Angels. Another group of UK Hells Angels was known as the Nightingale Chapter, after the Nightingale Café the chapter had been born in.

The names I have bestowed on my biker chums are not the names I knew them by, although they are nicknames they used in their previous life on two wheels, more or less. Tanner was the first I befriended. He had, as it happened, grown up on Monks Hill estate, and was contemporary with Johnny Blunt, Tommy, Joe Paris, Len (the Morpeth gardener) and some others I knew. Tanner was from 'traveller' type stock, the tenth child. He always seemed restless and gypsy-like, using Romany slang all the time I knew him. He was also famous for having green teeth. We became very good friends. Tanner started hanging at 125, and that meant Porky and Cowboy did too.

Porky actually lived with his mum down the Selhurst Road. A big strapping bloke with a soft side, had his hair in what had become an old-school DA, held together with hair spray (I could never understand why he didn't use Brylcreem), he had been the 'Prez' back in the Pond Angels days. A penchant for psychedelic drugs was slowly changing Porky from the hairspray down (and in another annoying parenthesis I might add that, after further adventures with Porky in the mid-seventies, we parted ways and he went down a regrettable slide with less adventurous narcotics). I won't bother to tell you anything about Cowboy; poor old Cowboy would not add much to my story. Cowboy was basically a follower, his contributions to our little society being that he could get and keep any number of vehicles running.

There were other characters who hung out at the flat. One of them was called Jeff Tree, who would play a part in my story a bit further down the line. A friend from the more recent past was Chillum Jeff, who went under that moniker for the most obvious reason. After the demise of Morpeth Jeff had a dalliance with a girl I had split with recently. Jeff had a string of objects attached to an earring, and Janet (for that was her name) would often catch this string of objects with her shoulder bag or her own hair. Consequently, the earring was gradually cutting its way down Jeff's lobe. By the time of the Selhurst flat, Jeff's earring was long gone, as was Janet, but his lobe looked something like a pig's trotter with its two-part shape caused by the retreat of the earring.

Life was pretty simple at 125. Tanner and Porky were regulars for the simple reason that they had nowhere to call their own. I was that rare being with my own pad, as tiny as it was. There would be evenings spent there with a pound weight of Durban Poison spread out on the newspaper it came in, with Jeff making chillums using about ten Senior Service and an equal amount of the weed. He would light it up with a chant he'd picked up in India, 'Bom Shankar!' Thanks to Shiva for the chillum. And so on.

I got into a fair amount of 'crime' with the biker lot. We found a dairy that had a delivery in the middle of the night, which supplied us with milk, yoghurt and other goodies that we would place out of the flat's window on a ledge, partly to keep it cool as I had no fridge, and partly to keep it hidden. I found myself involved in other nefarious activities that came habitually to those guys, which I wouldn't have dreamed of getting into, but were explained as necessities to me. Like, for instance, stocking up on much-needed petrol. These were not major crimes, and no-one was hurt, not even private property . . . much.

Most importantly no-one got caught. I had an offence in the very recent past to think about, and unknown to me at this point, it was soon to come up and bite me on the arse. Another thing we did was drive over to a baker near a place called Mitcham. At about 11.30 at night the buns would come out of the ovens and you could knock on the baker's door, and buy a bag. You could buy anything actually, but our favourites were the fresh buns. We'd buy half a dozen each in paper bags. They would scrunch up to nothing and melt in your mouth one at a time. Ate 'em hot in the car. Don't forget we all had a terrible case of the dope munchies. And later we would all have a roaring gut ache.

By now I had for some time been the owner of another motorbike, another vintage special. It was a Panther 600cc single. The bike lived, with a starting problem, outside Endlesham Road for most of the time I was there. After I had moved to Selhurst I had Porky collect the combination for me and ride it back to SE25, me being a little apprehensive of being picked up at the time, because I had no licence and I had had the recent bust. When it arrived at Selhurst I sold it on as soon as possible. Fortunately, there were buyers among my new biker circle.

We did a lot of acid. I woke up one morning and Cowboy was standing over me with a cap of Strawberry Fields. 'I've just downed one of these, I need company.' Okay, that's today sorted out then. At weekends we would be hanging with the usual crew in one of the usual places, and then we'd come up with a scheme for the weekend. We'd recruit one or two others, and next evening take off in whichever vehicle or two were running. In this way we would find ourselves on the Isle of Sheppey in the Estuary, on the northern coast of Kent.

The guys had been before and Tanner was fond of an area called Blue Town, which is in Sheerness on the far side of the island. Back then this area was like a ghost town, with the added attraction of a funny name. It was the winter, probably January or February by now. We would drive down on the Saturday night, park up near the water and away from prying eyes, and after a few joints and a few laughs on the beach, we'd sleep. Some in the van, the riders on the beach, all of it freezing. The next morning when we were awake, we'd drop a tab. Then go for breakfast.

Around this time I met this lovely girl called Marianne. She was of Gaelic gypsy stock, with long dark locks, seventeen again, and lived with her mother. I had been round to their place for coffee. One weekend I asked her to come on one of our trips to the coast. Tanner and the boys always met at Change Gear to discuss our weekend forays, and it was here I had engaged Marianne to come along.

In 1970 a Headquarters & General Store at West Croydon had closed down and was reopened by an enterprising soul with an eye on current trends as Change Gear, like many boutiques at the time, an imitator of Biba. There was in fact a far more authentic place that had opened across the street called Bus Stop, which was part of a chain whose original store was next to Biba in Kensington.

Anyway, on the first floor of Change Gear was a cafeteria, and a new meeting place for both the riff raff and the dolly birds of Croydon. In fact, while young office girls spent their wages on satin jackets, Minnie Mouse shoes and hot pants – yes, it was the height of the hot pants trend – they had a general feeling that there was 'a lot of pot smoking going on in the café upstairs'. There was actually a lot less than people thought, but the reputation was based on the 'types' up there.

That evening Marianne, the boys and I headed for Hayling Island, a small island off the south coast opposite Portsmouth, in a van. This was another place that turned weird during the empty stretch of winter. Porky had come on someone's motorbike. On Hayling Island beach we crashed out, Marianne and I in the back with two of the guys up front. I awoke twice during the night to find that my companion, whom I had no libidinous intentions for (a mixture of respect, and the close proximity of the two up front), was squirmingly turned on. Nothing actually happened, so to speak, but I was pleased, and more than a little surprised, to find that this was going to be a 'happening' relationship.

We were awakened in daylight by a banging on the side of the van. Dozily we came to with the realisation that someone needed our attention urgently and that our two companions were absent. I opened the back doors and found that we were surrounded by cops with dogs. Okay, so far – we were just a young couple sleeping in a van on a beach. Just one detail: proof of ownership of the vehicle. In those days a form of ID was not necessarily requested, it came down purely to the ownership of the van. Now, the owner of the van wasn't there, our two friends having split somewhere early in the morning. Hence, some research was needed. The cops called in for a check on our names, and mine came up trumps . . . a warrant out for my arrest, for unpaid fines. Uh-oh. Sorry, sir, we are going to have to take you to the station.

Then some more shit hit the fan. It was ascertained that my girlfriend was sweet seventeen. This meant that as I had been arrested and held until the van ownership could be proved, Marianne had to be collected by a guardian. She protested that her birthday was the next day, as it was, but what's one day between you and the Law? Incredibly her mother was called, and had to make her way out to Hayling Island. Uh-oh.

I didn't see Marianne again that day. I waited in a holding room until my mates appeared. Tanner and Cowboy had risen early, dropped a tab each, and eventually wandered back to the van to be told by a bobby standing guard where I was. There they were, grinning, at the station, tripping off their nuts, and proving, thank you very much, that one of them was indeed the legal owner of the vehicle on the beach. Too late for poor Marianne, who was by then catching hell from her mother all the way back to Thornton Heath.

I was let go, with a promise to appear at some court on such and such a date to explain my tardiness in paying my fine, not for anything I had done that day. I was given a new court appearance date, left the police station – and I dropped my tab. Ooo-wee! Another strange wander around another strange seaside town on a cold winter weekend with some Hells Angels. With an extra twist of fate. For me, those weekend coast excursions in 1971 were like reliving my Rocker days, only with psychedelic drugs thrown in. After strolling around all day as if we were visitors from another planet, we might end up back at the beach, deep in some hokey philosophy. I do remember a conversation about shellfish dying in their millions and with their shells ending up as sand, the sea washing over the sand and forming pebbles, the sand making glass, life being all around us and everything being a circle. You dig?

I continued to see Marianne after that, but in secret, another one banned from seeing me by her mother. Cannot blame the lady.

Return to Sender

My days at Selhurst were numbered. There was the new court appearance I did not attend, and a change of address seemed most opportune. Somewhere I met Chris L. again, who had moved into a council flat in, of all places, New Addington. He and Holly had secured a three-bedroomed flat in a block in the 'newer' part known as the Fieldway Estate. They'd had their first baby, Justin, who was two years old. The flat had a really big living room, and all three of the family were using one bedroom, so that left a spare room for Chris to call an office, in the days when a home PC was in the dim and distant future, leaving, *voilà*, a spare room. I accepted an invitation to move in and became a lodger again.

The terms that Chris and Holly offered were more than fair, as in, I could live there rent-free. If I wanted to eat with them, when Holly cooked dinner, I paid a token board, something like a fiver a week. If I did not want to eat with them I didn't have to pay board. I had been vegetarian since the previous year, so if I paid Holly, I still didn't actually eat with them, I cooked myself eggs and chips. If I was on hard times, and paid nothing, Holly *still* insisted I make myself sandwiches, so I lived on cheese and raw onion, something she had introduced me to. So – I was a lazy veggie, living on egg and chips or cheese and onion sarnies, depending on whether I was paying Holly my stipend or not. Perhaps not as healthy as the previous year's muesli at Morpeth, but what friends they were. My only contribution in the early months was to paint full-size Disney cartoon characters along the walls of the hall, for the entertainment of young Justin.

For a few months of this time I took a job in a leather tannery, which was about the weirdest thing I could have done as a vegetarian, especially one who had gone veggie in response to an acid experience outside a butcher. The job was really horrific. Every room in the tannery was huge, with the floor about six inches deep in some noxious watered-down chemical, necessitating the wearing of Wellingtons. The work mostly consisted of hours of slinging 'splits' – skins – that were soaked in said chemical into a kind of electronic mangle to squeeze out the excess moisture. A repetitive process involving, say, fifty slippery and smelly elephant splits, each of incredible weight. Monotony was not the word. I grew muscles for a while. The other occasional tasks I'll not bother to go into, but there were two particularly cheerful things about the job. One was the most indescribable stench that was omnipresent. The other was that here and there were graphic coloured posters warning about the early signs of anthrax. I didn't last long.

I was still going out with Marianne, against her mother's wishes, but not to her knowledge. We even spent some time in a cottage down in Kent that belonged to Marianne's aunt, a lovely rustic getaway, and not much of a risk for us, although not affording much of an escape if we were found out either. Eventually my selfishness and an encroaching acid paranoia split us up.

A little time after I'd broken up with Marianne I met her ex-boyfriend, an old mate of mine. Well, he laid the bombshell on me that she had been a virgin all the time she was with *him*, and that I was the first. *What*? I'd had no idea. I felt like shit. After some more time I heard that she had enrolled in a theological college. Not far removed from a convent?

While we were still together Marianne and I shared a couple

226

of acid trips. One was on a beautiful day in the summer of '71 in Shirley Hills – remember my trip the previous Christmas? This was my last ever trip. At the end of the day I was coming back late to the Addington flat. I got off the bus at the usual stop, and decided to take a short cut. Ducking into a lamppost-lit alleyway, I found myself walking in a direction that I was unfamiliar with. To my horror I realised the acid was still lingering. I pressed on but found myself suddenly in what seemed like someone's back yard, and then seemingly a maze of alleyways and dead ends. At this point I thought I heard – no, *I heard* – the coarse voices of a gang of Skinheads, in pursuit. Odd cries and shouts that sounded like they were nearing their prey. Voices echoed off the drab buildings. I was more lost than ever. Then at some point I emerged out of an alleyway and knew where I was! At that point the voices stopped, and, gasping and shaking with relief, I realised perhaps no-one had been there after all.

Chris and Holly were asleep when I let myself in. I climbed into bed, most likely after a cheese and onion sarnie. Insomnia laid her cold clammy palm over my heart and I lay trying to stop the whirling thoughts in my head. My life started to flash before me, exactly like it had when I had nearly drowned in a pool when the junior school were trying to teach us to swim at ten years old.

This time it was in colour; when I was ten it had been in monochrome. The thoughts sped up out of my control, getting faster and faster, as though it was too fast for it to be my own doing. At the peak of this sped-up Pathé newsreel it all suddenly stopped, and what was left was blackness. By that I don't mean I was alone in the blackness, I mean there was blackness and there was not me. Exit stage nowhere. There is and never was any memory of the next . . . however long.

When I came to all was calm. Then I floated up to the ceiling of that little room, and took a long look at myself lying on the bed under that single sheet in winter. I then faced everything thoughtless and unkind that I had ever done and resolved to never do it again, never to act like that again.

Acid was a different kettle of fish from all the other drugs I was doing. In a very real way it was not recreational as far as I was concerned. It was the one drug I was going to give up (there would be plenty of new ones to *take* up in the future), as I had learned all I could from doing it. From now on I was all set to be a better person.

Fat chance of that lasting.

Follow the Yellow Brick Road

During my stay at Chris and Holly's flat I spent a lot of time with a guy named Sebby. He was a Palestinian, and if you knew him well enough it would emerge that he had been a refugee from the Six Day War of 1967. Sebby had worked at Allders department store at the same time as me, and when he needed work again, Bob and I recommended him to Phonodisc in Ilford. I even wrote out on a piece of paper the exact route to take in order to get from Croydon to Ilford without paying any fare, which is what we did. On his very first day he was stopped by a representative of the railway police, and being unsure of what line of spiel to give, showed the guard the piece of paper. Sebby got busted. But at least he now had a job, so he could pay his fine.

A year later Sebby had a studio flat in Croydon, and it was there I would crash if I didn't want to make the bus journey back to Addington. It was far cosier to bed down at Sebby's and get stoned. We both liked to talk, and we would roll joints, play albums, and lie in bed rapping until the early hours. We would crash normally before the end of the last long-player side. Our favourite to go to sleep to was an album by Harvey Mandel called *Cristo Redentor*. This was one we both had stolen copies of from Phonodisc. We talked of many things, and sometimes he would peel off into a rant about Zionism. Although I knew little of what he was talking about, it was obvious he had experienced a trauma most of us in the West can only read about.

Sebby's surname was Mansour. Sometimes I would kid him

by saying, 'Mansour but woman sweet.' Yeah, I've always been a barrel of laughs.

* * *

Meanwhile, Alan and I were about to set off on another adventure. The West Coast of England had always held a fascination, been a pull. I'd been as far as Devon for holidays with my parents. The further horizons suggested tales I'd heard from the handful of 'on the road' Beats I'd known in the mid-sixties. George the Painter had always talked about being 'on the road', much of which was blown out of proportion. After I'd read *On the Road* by Jack Kerouac I realised the book was about cars. It was as much about cars as Chuck Berry's songs. We just did not have that love affair with cars over here. But we did have Beats talking about being 'on the road'. They had borrowed the expression from Kerouac and Cassidy, but they were referring to *hitching*. I always thought this amusing.

By '71 I had still not done much hitching, the hitch to the festival at Bath being a one-off. So, thinking it about time, and having plenty of time at my disposal, I got together with Alan in a plan to hitch to Cornwall. Checking two boxes at the same time, so to speak: hitting the road *and* Cornwall. Alan by now was a full-on freak, the vestiges of Mod having been submerged beneath a denim get-up on which he had practised his embroidery. Yes, Alan was becoming his own walking art installation. We had heard a bit about Newquay from Sun and Linda who had spent the previous summer there. They came back with stories of people making surfer beads for a living, spending the summer without shoes, like, totally *getting away*. It sounded good, and we were going to give it a try. Not the shoeless bit, but the getting away.

On the day of our planned start Alan showed up with another

head we knew called John Hudd. *What*? This John character, a hanger-on at the best of times, had just decided he had nothing better to do for a few weeks, and he would tag along. And Alan didn't seem to have had the gumption to tell him to go home.

Nor did I. Now, two young men with a fair amount of hair and faded Levi's will find it hard thumbing rides on the open road. It was true then; now I'm not sure it's even legal. But *three* young men? Forget about it. So John Hudd was going to tie his hitch to our post and ruin our possibility of getting to Cornwall any time soon.

I do not remember how far we got before deciding walking to Cornwall was not what we had intended. We pooled the little money we had – that is, Alan and I pooled our money – and we got on a train at some tiny little station in the middle of nowhere. I don't mean we left John behind, I mean we paid for his ticket. Ho-hum. Somehow we eventually arrived in Newquay. Now, the town of Newquay in those days was much nicer than it is now. If you go there today it's a lot like Croydon by the ocean. Shopping malls, pedestrianisation, new town, kids' meals in gastro pubs, you get the idea. Back then it was a very cool town. A charming old smugglery town. It wasn't quite as arty as St Ives, but it was romantic enough for us.

We had so little money by then that we bought some bread and cheese in a supermarket and made a meal, as they say in the old paperbacks. In the evening we managed a beer or two in a pub along the front. I caught sight of myself in the mirror behind the bar; my face was burned and my hairline was bleached. It had been a hot summer so far, and I had never seen myself like this. Lucky I didn't suffer sunstroke, which was something I had done a couple of times before. My clothes were dirty and so was I. It was hotter down here than we expected, and the heat and grubbiness, the tiredness and the feel of the open air on my skin, felt like what I imagined a trip to southern Europe would be like. We may as well have been in Italy. For a glorious few days I was really on the road.

After the pub we found ourselves on some sand dunes among a bunch of other travellers doing the same thing. Among the sleeping bags, one of which was set alight by a careless smoker bedding nearby, there was a great camaraderie and much laughter and good times. But the next morning there was a problem that was beginning to get serious. Alan had been complaining about a toothache since London, and it had reached a pain threshold that needed seeing to. Why, oh why, did you leave London with a toothache, Alan?

In the next couple of days we made it back to London, and we ditched John Hudd. Now at this time Bob 'n' Hilary were still residing in the flat in Balham. Alan had this idea. We would impose on their hospitality for a night's rest, so that Alan could get his teeth seen to, and no-one in Croydon would ever know we had come back from Newquay! We were still on the road! From Balham we would hitch, now that there would only be two of us, to the Kent Weald, and engage in a season of hop picking. I had heard much about the hop picking season from my pal Tanner. Apparently Tanner used to go down and do hop and apple picking among the gypsies and travellers in Kent. I mentioned he was a kind of gypsy type.

Alan got the molar mauled and we reconvened in Balham, Gateway to the South. In the morning Bob saw the two of us off with a hearty breakfast. It just happened that he decided to have us wash the whole collation down with some herbal tea. Neglecting to tell us that the herbal mixture was a powerful laxative. Thanks, Bob, very humorous.

As far as getting rides went, we were very lucky. However, we had to make many, many stops along the way! The following morning we woke in a field that had seemed innocuous enough in the pitch of the night before, but apparently housed a bull in the opposite corner. Over the fence we go . . .

Our destination was somewhere near Goudhurst or Cranbrook. Picturesque Kent. We found a remote farm, and it was blackberry season, somewhere in between hops and apple season. And they were very hard to pick. A row of corrugated iron huts faced a hard dirt clearing that the pickers used to barbeque their supper over a bonfire in the evening.

Alan and I were handed a basket each and told 'ten bob a basket-load'. Boy, did we do badly. Barely filled a basket by lunch the first day. The experienced pickers were making serious dough. They had their whole families out there, with little kids helping. They had it down like a profession. I suppose it was, for them. At day's end the other pickers felt sorry for us and let us share the baked spuds they were cooking over the fire. It was a bracing and moving experience. The hut was something else, however. Alan and I lay on our truckle beds and listened to the sounds of large soft animals thumping against the walls of the corrugated iron. We would open one eye and check the door for signs of it giving in every now and then. It may have only been big field rats, but we did not relish the idea of sharing our hut with them.

Blackberry picking was something we neither got good at, nor did for very long. Within no time we were back in south London, in the pubs, and spinning yarns about roughing it around the country.

Kick Out the Jams

I was living with Chris and Holly and cooking up schemes with Chris, who worked during the day. He was after all a family man, but he yearned to smash the establishment with a flame burning as bright as ever. Under his influence I read *Soledad Brother*, *Seize the Time* and *If They Come in the Morning*, this last being Angela Davis's book and manifesto. They were basically militant black power tomes from the USA. I mixed these with books by Richard Neville and Germaine Greer, and other flights of thought from the counterculture, along with a steady diet of the underground press; *IT*, *OZ* and *Frendz*.

Chris and I became members of the Angela Davis Defence Committee, and when she was freed we looked for another movement. Davis was a black American activist, a member of the Communist Party, and associated with the Black Panther Party. A feminist and a UCLA professor, it was her membership of the CP that got Ronald Reagan, then state governor, to have her banned from teaching in California. Then she was tried and acquitted for an involvement in the abduction-leading-to-murder of a US judge by the Soledad Brothers. She spent eighteen months remanded in county jail, a victim of racism, sexism and Californian right-wing politics. Chris wanted to continue with something of our own and he suggested we start a magazine. He had a duplicating machine at work, the employment of which was especially cheeky as his job was for a governmental agency that would have looked askance at the agitprop stuff we were producing. We wrote articles, went and typed them on borrowed typewriters using stencilling paper, and ran off pages on his duplicator – a messy, inky forerunner of today's printer. Another friend of mine got a few hundred sheets done on a proper printer at his college in Wood Green.

The mag was called *Red Fist & Bust*. The *Red Fist* part represented Chris's half of the mag, a wholly political diatribe based on the American Black Power model, but geared towards England. We had come across a load of plastic badges and they sported a red fist on a brown background, nothing else. So if we were called *Red Fist*, the buttons would serve as promotion when we gave them away (they were cheap for us to buy). The *Bust* half of the mag was so called because my world centred round the Croydon environs' 'head' society, which was fraught with busts, false arrests and bad drug deals. So, *Bust* dealt with one's rights within the law, what drugs to avoid, squatting, recipes, poetry . . . you get the idea. It was my version of a local underground paper. I didn't know it at the time, but such things were emerging all over the country.

I would take a bunch of the printed magazines down to the Star and dish them out for free. The Star was always full of plain-clothes coppers, and we would write about them with as much 'knowledge' as we could make up, giving these guys under cover plenty to read about right there among the freaks they were trying to bust or plant. Questions started to be asked among the clientele as to who produced these magazines. The landlord of the pub was hassled for information he didn't have. People brought in from the Star under suspicion of buying or selling dope were asked, 'Do you know where these magazines originate from?' along with the usual 'Okay, we've got you bang to rights, where'd you get the hash?'

One evening I was hauled into the station after being overheard at the Star arranging to score some dope. They left me stewing in a cell for some hours before my interrogator came in, thinking I was softened up and scared, and tried to accuse me of drug dealing, thus allowing me to show him my temper. Oddly, my throwing the chair I'd been sitting on across the cell and exclaiming expletives seemed to do the trick. I was let go with a warning. They had no idea I was the political agitator.

My old mates the Angels bought a bunch of the *Red Fist* buttons, paid for them, then distributed them for free at the Star and the Greyhound, which was emerging as both the rock venue to supplant the Star, and later as a place to hang out. At the Greyhound we saw the unbelievable MC5 for the first time of many after their move to the UK. They were the most hallowed band of the White Panthers, the militant group I was attempting to align myself with. The Panthers had started in 1968 in Detroit, in allegiance to the Black Panthers, and had caught the imagination of a small group of people over here mainly connected with the London underground press. The editor of *IT* at the time was Mick Farren, a one-time singer with a band called The Social Deviants who had turned author. Mick stayed a figurehead for the UK White Panthers, but was no longer hands-on by the time I got involved. The extent of his involvement may have been to incite small riots at various rock festivals, outside the main gates of which his new band, the Pink Fairies, would set up, while promoting the idea that all festivals should be free. The man who organised the White Panther Party in the UK lived in Abbey Wood in south east London, in his parents' council house, and his name was John Carding. It was John whom I eventually got in touch with to start my own chapter, which would be called the White Panthers Croydon/Bromley Chapter. John would later move into the world of London's underground press, following in Farren's footsteps at *IT*.

Of the guys from my Selhurst days who were helping me distribute buttons, without being asked, my biggest help came from Jeff Tree, who had become my shadow at this time and joined me in the White Panther Party. He would later join me, and some of the West London Panthers, in the London Central Committee formed by John Carding. It was during this time that a group of schoolgirls in the bar of the Greyhound asked about the Red Fist Movement, while I earnestly tried to explain the politics, wondering if I was getting through. After a while one of them said, 'When is the initiation ceremony?' Stopped dead in my tracks by the excited look in her and her friends' eyes, I endeavoured to explain that there was no such thing. That was the moment I understood Charlie Manson . . . and a strange truth about human nature.

In the first issue we even printed Chris's address! We stopped that with issue two, but it wasn't long before Chris and I noticed a car parked twenty-four hours a day outside the block of flats. *Special Branch*. What an honour! What was I thinking, on the run from a warrant?

Eventually Chris and I decided we needed to print two different mags. He wanted to move more in the direction of local community action. He launched *Community Press*, at a time when he could afford to get the whole mag printed offset lithographic. In fact, we had discovered a good 'underground'-minded litho press at Notting Hill, right on Ladbroke Grove, called Crest Press. We had been introduced to this printer by Jamie Reid, who was producing his own mag, *Suburban Press*, out of his flat in Norwood. Jamie didn't know anyone else in my sphere, and seemed to be solely engaged in activities that he had started while a student at Croydon Art School. He was focused. A few months older than me, and more of an intellectual, Jamie's artistic vision would stay on course till the present day, passing through a period in the seventies when his designs would influence the world during the punk revolution, for which he is best known. His anarchistic vision continues with his involvement and direct action from the campaign against the poll tax on to the anti-war demonstrations against Bush and Blair. At the same time he is considered a major modern artist.

Jamie's mag was more of a Situationist-inspired effort, and the illustrations within reminded me of the *Anarchy* mag that Paul Pawlowski had produced in the sixties. I got to know Jamie quite well, and wrote some articles for *Suburban Press*.

My own mag became *Street Sheet*, a continuation of *Bust*. *Street Sheet* would become the voice of the White Panther Party Croydon/Bromley Chapter, and I would continue my burgeoning association with the chapter based in Ladbroke Grove, the West London White Panthers. I could only afford to have a few pages printed litho and the rest would still be duplicated by my friend at college in Wood Green. For the few litho pages, saved for the bits of artwork commissioned or done by myself, I cruised up to Ladbroke Grove and Crest Press. Jamie had introduced me to the press and often he would be there getting his stuff done too. He would tell me about his friend from college days called Malcolm who had started a rock 'n' roll shop called Let it Rock in the Kings Road. Upset Teddy boys had given him a rough time because he'd got some details wrong on the suits he'd made for them. Malcolm needn't have worried, for greater things were to come, with Jamie's visionary help, and the help of Malcolm's wife, Vivienne Westwood.

* * *

One day Alan told me he had heard from Linda and Sun. They were living in a caravan on a farm in a remote part of Buckinghamshire. Alan had written to Linda and set up a meeting for a couple of weeks later at Finch's on the Portobello Road, a pub we had all known for as far back as any of us could recall – it sprang immediately to mind as the place to meet – and the four of us later took a train and a couple of buses back down to their caravan in the High Wycombe woods.

Straight away Linda and I had shiny eyes for each other. Over the coming weeks we kept our growing feelings to ourselves as Alan and I habitually travelled up to W11 to meet our chums and go on to spend the weekend at the caravan. The habit became fortnightly: Finch's; the Dog Shop on Blenheim Crescent for head shop supplies; the train to Bucks; and slowly but telepathically Linda and I were planning on running away. Meanwhile, our fortnightly stay at the caravan was a fun weekend escape comprising occasional forays to the nearby pub (which had a comfortable toilet), fetching water from an outside tap, Sun's excellent cooking and playing music. Oh yes, and Linda attempting to help me ride an ornery pony that preferred trying to run me into the trees. She was a naturally good rider, could ride anything with or without a saddle. And there I was, sticking out at a ninety degree angle from the side of this pony, stiff as a board, while the creature trotted happily through the wood, painfully introducing me to every tree along the path.

One Monday morning I lingered at the caravan after Alan had left and Sun had gone to work, and Linda doubled back from her job. Despite the moment of frustrated passion, we did not dive into bed, instead spending the day around the town. Planning, planning. When our secret was finally out, Linda was left to deal with it on her own. Linda and Sun had some kind of blow up during the week when Alan and I weren't around, and she moved to her parents' home in Kent.

Street Sheet would continue through a move out of Chris and Holly's flat and into Mum's new place in old Selsdon, the bungalow she and Fred had bought in the same street where Hamish's little sister, Kirsty, lived with her mum. I had not yet dealt with my outstanding fine; the Special Branch were taking more and more of an interest in Chris and me; it was time for us to enter one of our periods of going our separate ways. He and Holly would be at my and Linda's wedding the following April, but we had no idea it was the beginning of a very long time of Chris and me disappearing from each other's lives. While at Mum's I got involved in a certain little episode involving a cigarette packet.

Squatting and Plotting

In 1971 the West London White Panthers lived in a squalid terrace at 93 St Stephen's Gardens, off Westbourne Park Road, and I found myself up at their abode quite regularly. The people who actually lived there were a couple called Richard and Vicky, who actually ran the local Panthers, with the help from a musician called Steve Gibbons. My days up at Ladbroke Grove would include getting involved with a Free Food Programme that the Panthers operated under the newly-built Westway. Basically we were giving plates of brown rice and vegetables to poor local kids, with no political motive at all. At the same time as this I was still avidly reading the major London underground press, which included *Frendz*.

Frendz had a mail order page, where you could send postal orders and cheques to buy T-shirts; special king-sized rolling papers with the Stars & Stripes on them; chillums, legal even if what was smoked in them wasn't; low-run publications by young writers; reprints of Aleister Crowley's books by small publishers; cookbooks that involved cooking with marijuana; the I-ching, tarot cards, comix (always with an 'x') and *bootlegs*. Among the bootlegs *Frendz* advertised were two LPs that I wanted. One was a concert of Bob Dylan at the Royal Albert Hall in 1966 and the other was a collection of rare tracks by Elvis Presley that included a song cut at Sun Studio that had never appeared anywhere before. So I sent my money and then proceeded to wait. And wait . . .

Linda and I had moved in to a flat in a terraced house in a quiet residential area of Streatham. We had both done our time back with our parents while we waited for our chance to be together. She had taken a post with a theatrical agency in Mount Street in Mayfair, which had started as a temp job and turned full time. It was run by an ex-actress called Maggie Johnston, whose film-director husband Al Parker had started the agency. The agency looked after people as disparate as Lindsey Kemp, Linda Thorson (the then-current *Avengers* girl Tara King), James Mason and Helen Mirren. Maggie herself would call up if Linda was absent from work and berate her about how she was missed. Once when we were at Mum's she called asking for Linda and had an argument with Mum. Maggie was a law unto herself.

Linda would take detours on her way home from work to call in at *Frendz* in Portobello Road to see if they had my bootleg LPs yet. They never did, but they would always ask her if she wanted to run their mail order page.

Our landlady in that Streatham flat was a fastidious Hungarian who had escaped the violent revolution there against the Russians in the fifties. Her house was immaculate, though dark and musty. Thick plastic was nailed to the stairs with great brass tacks, so the stair carpet would never wear out, but tended to be rather slippery.

She did not like the fact that we were unmarried. Two girls lived in a flat on the floor above, and they were not allowed any visitors at all. One morning a Panther cohort called on us to go off together to a demo over in Dartford, Kent. Our landlady saw the three of us leave, and as it was so early, she assumed our friend had stayed the night. She gave us a lecture for having a man stay with us. By this time we were becoming less surprised by her Victorian attitude.

We had also put up a couple of posters, one of which was a rather good one of Angela Davis, a leftover from my involvement with Chris the previous year. To our landlady this picture of an attractive black woman just represented communism! On

242

invasively nosy visits to our rooms, she would rail about the poster. She would end her rant with 'These people are so miserable. Look at the eyes. The eyes, they look to me!'

Where had I heard that before?

After two months of living under the watchful eye of our nosy landlady, we moved out and got married. Something we felt would alienate some of our anti-establishment friends but would help us in the straightjacket world of 1972. We loved each other and that made it real. The West London White Panthers – Richard, Vicky and Steve to be precise – had moved to a squat in Chalk Farm and invited us to join them. We shifted our arses really fast.

The last issue of *Street Sheet* came off the presses after Linda and I had moved out of the south London area. Without me the energy dissipated and waned, no-one wanting to take the reins. I was disappointed in, though not surprised by, the other Croydon/Bromley Panthers, but my interests were elsewhere by now.

The 68 bus used to have 'Chalk Farm' on its destination plates. It came out of South Croydon garage, so it had been a familiar sight for my entire life. When regular gigs started at the Roundhouse in the late sixties, friends and I would take the 68 there and back – a very long journey. So Linda and I packed as much as we could into a couple of bags, sat on the back seat on the top deck of a 68, and rode all the way to a new life.

We never looked back.

* * *

We moved the whole shaboodle into this spacey empty room on the top floor of a house in Allcroft Road, threw Angela Davis and some other posters over the biggest holes in the walls, laid some carpets on the floor and got the record player working off the light socket. Linda and I immediately became the reclusive couple living a bit 'luxuriously' on the top floor.

I started working at *Frendz* on Portobello (hello, the 31 bus), sorting out the mail order page. It immediately became apparent why my two bootlegs had never been sent. The mail order department was dormant, and in as much disarray as the mag itself. There was far too much energy being spent on acquiring advertising copy to pay the print bill to chase a bootleg supplier as well. *Frendz* at the time was peopled by a fascinating group including Nick Kent, who was the music reporter, and Penny Smith, the photographer. Some of the *Frendz* staff went over to the *New Musical Express* when *Frendz* folded, and, frankly, changed the face of music journalism in the UK.

The biggest surprise with Chalk Farm squatting was how together everything and everyone was. At first I was apprehensive, wondering how safe it would be, how long it would last, and wanting security. But in under a fortnight, I felt as safe as houses, despite visits from the Law, visits from surveyors and general hassles with drunken visitors and violent strangers. Of course, it helped having no rent to pay, being surrounded by friends and having so much community activity going on around us. As for the Panthers, activity was soon at a minimum. The Camden squatting scene was about survival, and was enough activity for all concerned in itself, so it seemed.

Sid Rawle personally visited us. Sid Rawle's Diggers had the whole area 'sussed'. Sid had moved to London from St Ives in the mid-1960s and become involved in the alternative scene. He was noted in these circles for his refusal to take drugs. Initially involved with a group called Tribe of the Sun, he formed the Hyde Park Diggers, campaigning on the issues of land use and land ownership, concerns that were central to the rest of his life's actions. He also formed the Digger Action Movement with Barry Norcott and John Gillatt, which brought him into contact with John Lennon.

In 1970, Lennon invited Rawle to establish a commune on

Dorinish, a small island in Clew Bay, Ireland, which Lennon had owned since 1967. After surviving Atlantic storms, the commune eventually disbanded in 1972 after a fire destroyed their main stores tent. Lennon contributed money towards Rawle's communes and other projects, and was reputed to have financed the film *Winstanley* about Gerrard Winstanley, a charismatic leader of the Diggers movement, in which Rawle had a role as a Ranter, which suited him admirably.

During the early 1970s, Rawle became increasingly involved in the London squatting scene and the free festival movement. He was involved in organising the Windsor Free Festivals and the 1974 Stonehenge Festival, together with Bill 'Ubi' Dwyer. Dwyer himself, an irrepressible Irishman, had been imprisoned in Australia for activities connected with LSD, and deported to Ireland. He was the man originally asked by John Lennon to help him set up the commune, and was involved in the Freedom Press group and their *Anarchy* magazine. He witnessed the tearing down of the fences, by Farren's Panthers, at the Isle of White festival in 1970, which led him to set up the Windsor Free Festival on former common land that had been poached by the monarchy. He and Rawles were imprisoned in 1975 to prevent the violence that had ensued during the suppression of the free festival in 1974.

Sid took no shit from the Law. After we'd been at Allcroft for a few days, some of Sid's guys came round and showed us how to get this and that together. We seemed to have one of the most together squats in the area. There were two houses. The one next door to us had running water, a loo that worked, gas and a cooker in the kitchen. So, for the essentials of eating and shitting, we all went there.

Our house had electricity, so I got to play my records, which was nice. House number two turned on their electric at one time, but the Law saw the lights and came round and told them to turn them off or they'd 'get done'. But it seemed to be cool for us to have lights, which we couldn't figure. Neither house had a working bath. In Kentish Town there were some old-fashioned 'slipper' baths – public baths, the first and only time I ever experienced such magnificent Victorian establishments. You paid your money, you waited your turn, and you went in to a bathroom where the tub was brimming with hot water. If you needed more water you knocked on the wall. Although, I have to say, I personally had an urgent reason for such trips as I had fallen victim to the dreaded head lice, an epidemic of, not Camden Town, but of *Frendz* magazine, where all the Ladbroke Grove-ites had the little tenants.

The whole area around Kentish Town, Chalk Farm and Mornington Crescent was grey, bombed-out, filthy and dull. Among the 'rubble' were squats that had been turned into hippy tea rooms, dark dungeons of runaway hangouts reeking of musk or patchouli oil. In these dark cellars would be huddles of young coll-eyed females in long imitation-Biba dresses, with poker-faced seriousness written from their lank hair to their sandaled feet. This was not like where we'd come from. These were not our people. I felt out of my safety zone. We had left behind our dopey friends, but who were these doped-out fiends? I can now look back and see that these were the children of the late sixties pan-UK movement, lost and unsmiling in their innocent fear. Mornington Crescent was a catchment area for England's waifs and strays, and they had all arrived from their own private Croydons. There was something telling Linda and me that we hadn't arrived at our destination. Camden Town was in fact a fare stage on the way to Ladbroke Grove. We had a feeling we wouldn't be here for long; we were moving on soon, and these strangers would stay strangers.

* * *

Not long after we moved to the Camden house, this cat who was staying at one of the houses OD'd; he got picked up by an ambulance and they pumped his guts. He gave the Law our address, and round they came. First they got into house number two, which was where four girls lived, and the cops left their phone numbers on the wall! Ha ha, oink oink. Some hours later they came back and visited house number one, our house. A rap on the door, footfalls on the landing and early morning sunlight through the windows woke me up. I kept my eyes shut as the door opened. A voice said, 'They're asleep, let's go.' And they left!

I only found out later it was the fuzz. Blew my mind. Where I had recently come from they'd have kicked me half to death in my bed. I mean, the Croydon CID had a rep back then that would make the fuzz over in NW5 seem like the proverbial vicar's tea party.

At house number two there was a tap and sink in a room next to an outside unused toilet, and generally I used that to have the occasional cold wash and to brush my teeth. Over the garden wall in the morning and the evening with my toothbrush and then back again. One of the hassles with squatting: one morning I discovered that this little outhouse had been allocated to the dogs that lived with the people in the house. So that's why my shoes stunk that morning. I had trodden in some dogshit the night before in the dark.

The girls in house number two had not been part of the White Panthers movement back in St Stephen's Gardens, so I don't know where they came from. They seemed to cause a lot of trouble; one of them in particular was always shouting her mouth off, and bringing disrepute to our little scene. The idea with squatting was to be cool. The house on the other side of us had a young couple with a baby living in it. Not squatters, straights. These were the days when a whole house could be rented cheap in tumbledown neighbourhoods like Chalk Farm and Kentish Town.

The couple were always moaning about the behaviour of the girls in the house on the other side of us. We could have got on with our neighbours okay if it wasn't for the girls. For a while this couple had a mate staying with them who had just come out of nick for some sort of violence against another human being. He was on probation, and couldn't afford to get back into trouble, or he would be whipped back in for a long stretch. They were cheap gangsters. Living next door to squatters.

One night we had a couple of our friends from south of the river staying with us – Alan, and John Hudd, our 'on the road' buddy. Two of the girls from next door had joined us; one of them was the mouthy one. I remember being in a corner of the room with Alan and John. Linda was on the bed, and the two girls were hanging out of our window, making a noise. We were all very stoned, so it was the worst sort of behaviour you could expect. Then the couple next door, the ones with the mate from prison, and the baby, arrived home and started getting out of their car. They looked up and told the girls to keep quiet. It occurred to us at the time that they had reasons of their own to lead a quiet life – not just the baby, but perhaps various other dodgy activities. Anyway, one of the girls, the annoying one, got sassy and shouted something back.

Suddenly the mate on probation came crashing through the front door of our house (security was slack), and we could hear him rushing up the stairs. He burst into our room and in true macho fashion strode over to where my two mates and I were sitting around stoned in the corner. He ignored the girls who had caused him to break in, and came straight up to the 'fellers'.

His opening salvo was, 'Okay who's going to lose an eye?'

This was very fearsome and worrying behaviour, to which a reply was impossible, given how stoned we were, and the fact that we weren't too keen on shouldering the responsibility for these stupid mares whom we had been telling to cool it, anyway.

Now, I was always the one with the front, the one who wanted to either cool the situation with a few well-chosen words, or to face the adversary off. In this case, a face-off was out of the question. The man was a Neanderthal with a pea-sized brain. I stood up to make peace, and was met instantly with a fist smashing into my face that almost knocked me out.

I fell backwards and nearly crumpled to the floor from where I had risen. At the same time, I did manage to observe the total lack of engagement of my two male friends, who retained their sitting position. Also the impartial behaviour of the two girls at the window. Welcome to the world of working-class behaviour, you middle-class hippy tarts. Thanks, see what you've done?

At the same time, the husband came blustering up the stairs in order to stop his mate from causing trouble and possibly bringing the Law down on us all, and getting his mate back in the clink. At least these seemed to be his motives. The brute had calmed down like a tranquillised dog after throwing the punch, and seemed to realise what he was doing. He was following his friend out, but only got as far as the top of our stairs when Linda, who had come to her senses a split second before the dolt had hit me, came through the door, throwing the beast, twice her weight, down the flight of stairs, followed by some very choice language. The wife had appeared at the front door by then, probably to get the men in her life back in order and out of potential trouble. The beast smacked into her at the bottom of the stairs, and his mate followed out the door in a flash. Linda – the only human being there that night who cared about me or had any guts. She could face down two hefty London gangsters and their bitch with the baby; she wasn't about to let it go that she'd seen her man dumped on the ground with a split lip. She was a hippy, but she was a force of nature.

When we got served a court order over the squat in Camden, Linda and I decided to make ourselves homeless (a totally different proposition in pre-1980s Thatcher Britain) instead of waiting for the outcome or going to court. In other words we just split, and left it all to anyone who cared. I had some signet rings stolen from a coffee table one night while we slept, reminding me that we were not, in fact, surrounded by loving hippies, but by people desperate for money. We sold editions of *Frendz* at a couple of summer rock festivals. Meanwhile some friends had moved into a flat on Tavistock Road W10, and we prevailed on their kindness and their invitation to crash on their floor until we could find a flat. When we settled into their place, I thought, right, that's it, we're 'here' now. By which I was thinking, Ladbroke Grove, this is where I want to be. Linda started working for the guy who then owned the indoor market at 253 Portobello, where I would later open a record stall after I quit *Frendz* in early '73.

Estate Agent

In Tavistock Road we lived in a two-roomed flat, and we were sharing one room with another couple, their two dogs and one cat (a kitten Linda and I had acquired). In the other room were our old friends Alan and John Hudd! It was one of those terraced houses where we went downstairs for the communal toilet and down further still for the communal bath. And the landlord came round every Friday for the rent, in cash. We were desperate for a place of our own.

Bruno, a small tough West Indian, ran his own flat agency and may or may not have had connections with notorious local landlords. The way it worked, you paid Bruno a sum of money in cash equal to the amount that you wanted to pay per week in rent. He then found you a flat and the money you paid became your deposit. If he didn't find a flat for you, or you found one another way, you got your money back. We had been to see Bruno and given him the princely sum of six quid. He had an office in Pembridge Road. Very soon after paying Bruno our deposit, John Hudd announced he was leaving Tavistock Road. So we could move into the room next door and share it with Alan.

Alan and I had never been as close after Linda and I got together. He felt betrayed in some way. Basically, his mate had broken up his other mate's relationship, and was now married to his *other* mate. If you see what I mean. We were friendly, but it was not the same as it had been. He was working on building sites at this time, and he even gave me some work on a site in Shepherds

251

Bush, my only time ever as a builder's labourer. At the weekends Alan was still spending his time around the old Croydon patch, which meant Linda and I had the room to ourselves.

So when we moved in with Alan we needed our deposit back from Bruno. We were living on very little money, as I was working at *Frendz* magazine, where I was back to earning £4 a week, and Linda had started working at 253, earning a proper wage. She and I were up in the *Frendz* office at 307 Portobello one weekday, and she called Bruno on the office phone. He told her, 'Don't come today. I don't have any cash today. I'll have it tomorrow.'

This may sound strange to the modern reader, but in the same way that £6 was enough for us to need it back straight away, it was also enough that a man in business could not have it to hand at his office. Actually, I thought it was a bit lame, and that he was fobbing Linda off. I called Bruno back, and we had a row. One of us put the phone down; it may have been me. I was mad, and I was going to get the money. At least that's what I thought.

We left 307 together and stumped up Portobello Road in the direction of Notting Hill and Pembridge Road. We didn't speak to each other, even when we saw Alan coming the other way, heading home from a morning's work on the building. Alan was bouncing towards us with his customary dancing swagger and cheesy grin. He naturally wanted to chat, but I wanted to keep the fury going. He was rabbitting away and I was thinking, 'Come on, Alan, come on.' He eventually seemed to understand my need to keep my temper flared. See ya, Alan.

It seemed to take forever. We finally reached Pembridge Road and turned right. Bruno's office was halfway down towards Notting Hill Gate and we strode in, Linda keeping up behind me.

Bruno had an outer office with a receptionist, very posh for his sort of operation. The receptionist peered up with a look of surprise through owl-like glasses.

'Can I *help* you?'

'We're here to see Bruno.'

'He's with someone at the moment . . .'

I ignored the secretary, the force of my thrust forward carrying me straight through the door to the inner office. Bruno's desk faced the door, and as I crashed into the room he rose to his feet, coming around his desk in a fluid non-stop motion before stopping to face me with his legs apart in a strong defiant pose. The middle-aged woman he had been interviewing sat looking shocked. Linda was behind me still. Without breaking my stride, with one swing I kicked Bruno in the crutch. It was like a goalkeeper's kick. My foot landed with full force in his knackers area, and I was six foot plus to his about five foot six. He stood stock still, unflinching, and stared at me. The kick hadn't moved him.

The client got up and made a beeline for the door. 'Call me,' said Bruno to her back.

It was at this precise moment, as my entire negative energy was spent with the violent kick, that I cooled off in an instant.

'Take it easy,' were his first words to me. He made a downward flapping gesture with both hands.

'We want our money . . . today!' I shouted. But I had lost my momentum.

Bruno made us sit while he coolly explained his need to return our deposit tomorrow, not today. No need to get het up. Okay, anything you say, Bruno.

Linda was probably glad the fuss had died out. So, we left, and Linda came alone the next day. I stayed away. While she sat opposite him, Bruno expounded on what a hothead I was. He said, 'I like your husband. But Brian should really watch his temper. I'm a cool guy but I don't care what happens to me. I have nothing to lose, so I can get arrested. Brian needs to calm down.'

To prove his point he got a gun out of a drawer and laid it down on the desk. He wasn't threatening Linda with it, he acted perfectly calmly. He was gentle and kind. He just wanted to let her know that if he by chance had used it on me, it wouldn't matter what might happen to him. I was very lucky.

* * *

I was blooded. As in, ready for London West Ten and West Eleven 1970s-style. We moved into the back room of the flat in Tavistock Road, which overlooked the gardens at the back of Tavistock Crescent, resting uneasily in the interim period before their erasure from existence, as London's Notting Hill awaited redevelopment after its sentencing to death.

An image from the time of living in that back room at Tavistock Road: a lady sweeping her back yard in Tavistock Crescent, watched by a semi-feral black-and-white tomcat and his gang. She steps back into her kitchen, comes back out with a bucket, throwing a sweeping arc of water across the yard while Tom and his whole gang run smoothly under the arc and away, bone dry. This happens *every day*.

Just like Tom and his gang, I now knew a sense of permanency. Developers could come and make the lady disappear, but us feral boomers were here to stay, if we could dodge the water in a graceful, cunning and optimistic enough way.

Some did, some did not. But I had found my spiritual home.

The Sun Sinks in the West

At last I was living in the streets described in 1963 by the *News of the World*. Immediately it was obvious: here was a patch with its own *peripherique*. The Harrow Road ran along the northern edge, paralleled by the Grand Union Canal just south of it. The Great Western railway headed out from Paddington as it began its journey to the West Country, also paralleling the above. At a point at the north-eastern corner of our area this westward railway joined with what was then the Metropolitan Tube line, an elevated section of the underground, which itself snaked south-westwards, among the rooftops of the slums, cutting diagonally through the area, towards the western extreme at Shepherds Bush. And at this point it met another road, running along our bottom perimeter, Holland Park Road, which ran back east towards the West End, passing Kensington Gardens and Hyde Park, changing its name along the way to the Bayswater Road. In fact this road was the old Oxford Road and divided W11 from Holland Park, which was a toffs' neighbourhood, and always had been. A road called Wood Lane divided the western side of our neighbourhood from a vast wasteland, with totter's yards dotted here and there, brick fields, Wormwood Scrubs Prison and park, White City greyhound racing track and of course, Aunty BBC.

A motorway had been constructed, for those wanting to motor west (clunk click every trip) instead of going by train (clickerty clack). The Westway was an elevated road that slashed across east to west over our heads on its way west and had, in fact, just been

255

opened before my arrival, under much protest from the top floor slum dwellers that had been forced to view the elevated road from their windows just yards away.

Over by the eastern wall was Westbourne Grove, which had the uneasy distinction of being in W2 and part of Westminster, where we could find a twenty-four-hour convenience shop, and a mile of curry houses, before we found ourselves in Bayswater.

And finally running north to south across our area was the grand thoroughfare of Ladbroke Grove, that developer's dream of the nineteenth century, with its secret gardens and crumbling piles, and running next to it like a frail little brother, squiggly old Portobello Road, the much maligned lane with a history and a memory all its own. At the southern edge we had Notting Hill, and in the north Kensal Green, the whole being North Kensington, a runt of an ignored section of the Royal Borough.

This was a village. While in the recent past I had met my friends at certain pubs and venues, now I would live in a village inhabited by similar souls. This was the place where the world's (not just the country's) waifs and strays, artists and artisans, musicians and poets, Jamaicans and Irish, hustlers and agitators, pimps and pros, cowboys and Indians, junkies and jugglers . . . lived in the same streets. It was a veritable conspirators' estate. Everyone had come home.

Now I lived within strolling distance from Rock On records on Golborne Road; Henekey's, the hippies' choice of pub; the Apollo, the scary West Indians' choice; the Mountain Grill, the choice of café; the Market, where I had once bought fur coats to sell back in Croydon; free gigs under the Westway, on the muddy scar of land left under the elevated concrete monster where there had once been dwellings; free gigs at the squatted Royalty Theatre; the Electric Cinema, with a hole in the roof and someone always ready for an argument; Finch's; Mike's, the second choice of café; and the Mangrove, on All Saints Road. I'd read about this in the underground press, how a court case and demonstrations had followed police harassment of this West Indian restaurant and meeting place in the heart of what would be the burgeoning Carnival in the years to come. How the owner of the Mangrove, Frank Crichlow, had once run the Rio, on Westbourne Park Road, where Christine Keeler and Stephen Ward scored their weed.

Our world would be dominated by the indoor market at 253 Portobello; Alchemy, the head shop; Ceres, the whole food shop; the Dog Shop, the older head shop; the Free Shop, under the Westway, leave what you don't want, take what you do; the little shop on the corner, L. Nagy, run by the Polish man; Forbidden Fruit, which used to be I Was Lord Kitchener's Valet, where I had come with Chris to buy a guards' jacket; the convents, one on either side of Portobello as you ran out of shops heading north, one off Ladbroke Grove, and little Franciscan and Carmelite chapels hidden away; wine bars before they were trendy, like Finch's on Kensington Park Road; Harpers, the electrical shop where one of the two ageing owners would fix anything from a kettle to an iron and not charge.

This is where I'd come to visit the White Panthers, now gone, taking part in the Free Food Programme, where now stood the Westway Theatre. Where I could look up at crumbling yet statuesque old buildings no longer in use, like the doomed Sylchester Road Public baths, of late Victorian splendour, com-memorating, as it did, a more philanthropic past, later smashed to the ground, even after it was listed, by marshals of the Thatcher regime; the quarter once known as the Piggeries where squatters had claimed sovereignty and called it Frestonia; breakers' yards where *Steptoe and Son* had been filmed.

We watched films at the Electric that had been shot right on this location: *Performance*, *10 Rillington Place*, *West Eleven*, *Otley*, *Darling*, *Alfie*, *The L-Shaped Room* and *Blow-up*.

Saw the rock stars that had made the Grove their home, had

given it its tarnished reputation, or had recently left, like Marc Bolan, Twink, Steve Peregrine-Took, Pink Fairies, Hawkwind, Lemmy. Where the guy who had started the psychedelic group Quintessense advertised for a guitarist, stating that the candidate had to live in Notting Hill. He got five hundred applicants.

And down the Lane on busy Saturdays, we enjoyed the man with the green parrot that posed on tourists' shoulders; the old lady who sang along to opera 78s playing from a wind-up gramophone in a pram; the gypsy in his ornate caravan on Acklam Road, who told hundreds of customers their fortune, which always came true; and the endless buskers who mainly sounded like Cat Stevens.

Yes, this was a village where some of the boomers had come to stay. And I was one.

About Face

For the record, I have not seen or heard of Alan Young since the day he disappears from my story.

In 1976 a band I was playing in secured a spot on a BBC television show. Chris Lansdowne saw this and called the Beeb, from whom he got the number of a record shop I was working at. This led to him calling round to my flat. Neither he nor I had any way of knowing that this would be the last time we would see each other for nearly three decades. Our finding each other again after all that time inspired this book. Chris helped with essential details of our lives, filling in my memory.

Chris Reeves is still very much a part of my life. He and I had our biggest adventures in the decades that followed the timespan of the book. We have been soulmates since 1967. Chris, thanks for Gino's Coffee Bar.

Alan Male and I saw very little of each other after he moved out of W10 and went back across the River. There were some moments early on, but they grew less frequent. He died mysteriously in Brighton, where he had been living for some years.

Other people left my sphere and returned more recently, one of these being Johnny Blunt.

The girls? Tina, Kathy, Desiree and Rosalyn all married and have families.

Linda was my first wife, and we are still very good friends.

The last time I saw Dave was in the eighties, and he was running a studio in Thornton Heath. Tony Perry was a greengrocer.

Ronnie Diamond is still singing. Maurice is the guy who came up with the 'bomb site' analogy.

Jeff Tree, Monks Hill Tommy and Chillum Jeff have thrown off the mortal coil.

My mother and father have passed on to where they will not read this book.

Burmese Sun lives in my street. I don't think he will read it, either.

Colin Dipple? Call me.